THE HISTORY OF
REYNARD THE FOX

Here begynneth thystorye of reynard the foxe

In this hystorye ben wreton the parables / goode lerynge, and dyuerse poyntes to be merkyd. By whiche poyntes men maye lerne to come to the subtyl knoweleche of suche thynges as dayly ben vsed & had in the counseyllys of lordes and prelates gostly and worldly / and also emonge marchantes and other comone peple. And this booke is maad for nede and prouffyte of alle god folke / As fer as they in redynge or heeryng of it shal mowe vnderstande and fele the forsayd subtyl deceytes that dayly ben vsed in the worlde / not to thentente that men shold vse them But that euery man sholde eschewe and kepe hym from the subtyl false shrewis that they be not deceyued / Thenne who that wyll haue the very vnderstandyng of this mater / he muste ofte and many tymes rede in thys booke and ernestly and diligently marke wel that he redeth / ffor it is sette subtylly lyke as ye shal see in redyng of it / and not ones to rede it ffor a man shal not lyght ones ouer redyng fynde the ryght vnderstandyng ne comprise it wel but oftymes to rede it shal cause it wel to be vnderstande And for them that vnderstandeth it / it shall be ryght Joyous playsant and prouffitable

How the lyon kynge of alle bestis sent out his mandementis that alle bestis sholde come to his feest and court capitulo primo

The first page of the narrative of Caxton's *Reynard*

THE HISTORY OF
REYNARD THE FOX

TRANSLATED AND PRINTED BY

WILLIAM CAXTON

IN

1481

Edited with an Introduction and Notes by

DONALD B. SANDS

Cambridge, Massachusetts

HARVARD UNIVERSITY PRESS

1960

TO ERNESTINE

Two alternatives face the editor of a medieval prose work. He can present the text in modernized spelling and punctuation. If he does so, he slights the scholar. He can produce the text in diplomatic form and such is repellent to the general reader. Here the former alternative is taken. *Reynard the Fox*, which in all its various past editions is out of print, is a masterpiece in its genre. Because of its potentially wide appeal, it deserves to appear in the most easily read as well as the most historically sound version possible. The text that follows is an edition of the first printing of William Caxton's translation of the Middle Dutch *Die hystorie van Reynaert die Vos*. Background material, here presented in a three-chapter Introduction, summarizes all the best and all the modern studies devoted to Reynard as the hero of a comic beast epic. Since a great portion of the studies involved are in Dutch, they are, even with better-than-average library facilities, just as unavailable to the scholar as a modern edition of the text is to the general reader. The three introductory chapters, then, are the result of an extended effort to assimilate a complex and restricted field of scholarship; they also constitute an attempt to please the scholar in addition to the general reader, who, nevertheless, both in the writing of the Introduction and in the transcription of the text took precedence over everyone else.

Friends and colleagues had their part in the preparation of the following pages. Professors B. J. Whiting and Taylor Starck of Harvard read the complete work; Professor Whiting read parts of the Introduction several times. Mr. F. M. Palmer of the Widener Library was helpful with bibliographic problems, as was also the staff of Houghton Library. Dr. Curt F. Bühler of the Pierpont Morgan Library read the material concerning Caxton; Professor Leo Spitzer of Johns Hopkins made an emendation or

PREFACE

two in the portion of the Introduction where Old French literature is touched upon. Professor Edward L. Hirsh of Boston College did his best to rid the prose of the Introduction of stylistic
flaws. Needless to say, the presence of a spouse, as always in such
projects, provided the impetus that finally completed the edition.

D. B. S.

Boston College
November 1959

CONTENTS

THE HISTORY OF
REYNARD THE FOX

ILLUSTRATIONS

INTRODUCTION

CHAPTER I

THE GOUDA AND CAXTON EDITIONS

REYNARD is a folk hero engendered ultimately by the people even though as an epic figure his origins must be traced to monastic scholarship. He passed through the capable hands of two Flemish poets on his way to becoming the comic hero of an epic, but he has never lost his winning humanity. He in no way represents the little man, even though he is a protagonist of average proportions. He would be inappropriate as a sociological or political symbol, despite the fact that his first and last impulse is to survive and that he consistently portrays the innocently oppressed and only on occasion the oppressor. He is human enough to possess a streak of genuine meanness, a degree of unpredictability, and a devastating flair for fake humility. His loyalties are those of the blood — to Grimbert, his nephew, to Rukenaw, his aunt; the nicety of less primitive dedication is foreign to him. He is a Hamlet in reverse, one who in order to exist acts on impulse and reflects after the deed and then usually only along amoral lines. It is possible to admire him, but in conventional circles we would perhaps hesitate to voice our admiration, for he is dangerously kin to our asocial selves. He may well have made Caxton uneasy, for he takes leave of his animal hero with the words "And if anything be said or written herein that may grieve or displease any man, blame me not, but the fox, for they be his words and not mine."

William Caxton first printed his translation *The History of Reynard the Fox* in 1481. The work has no title page, but the printer's and translator's name, place of publication, and date of translation are to be found in the colophon. It runs, in the early modern English of the original:

Prayeng alle them that shal see this lytyl treatis / to correcte and amende / where they shal fynde faute / For I haue not added ne

3

INTRODUCTION

mynusshed but haue folowed as nyghe as I can my copye Whiche was
in dutche, and by me Willm Caxton translated in to this rude & symple
englyssh in thabby of Westmestre. fynysshed the vj daye of Juyn the
yere of our lord. M.CCCC.Lxxxj. & the xxj yere of the regne of kynge
Edward the iiijth.

These words are consonant with the known facts of Caxton's life.
That he printed *Reynard* in the Abbey of Westminster is probably not quite true; his printing press in 1481 seems to have been
located in a building near the west wall of the Abbey, which, since
it was such a conspicuous landmark, served as a sort of signpost
for the various shops clustered about it. Though Englishmen in
1481 used the word *dutche* to designate just about any Low German dialect, Caxton's statement in the colophon is correct in the
modern English sense because the original Reynard book from
which he made his translation was written in Dutch and published
in Gouda, Holland, in 1479.

In 1909 Seymour de Ricci was able to locate six copies of Caxton's first edition of *Reynard the Fox*: two in the British Museum,
one in the John Rylands Library in Manchester, one at Eton College, one in the possession of the Duke of Newcastle, and one in
the Christie-Miller collection at Britwell. A seventh copy there
may still be; one was catalogued in a James West sale of March
1773. De Ricci says that the present owner is "untraced," but adds
parenthetically "Was it Caxton's edition?" The specter of a
seventh copy, at any event, keeps alive the fox hunt in English
bibliographic quarters. William Blades in his *Biography and Typography of William Caxton* presents a table of editions printed
by Caxton with the number of copies known to exist for each
edition. Of one hundred two editions thirty-eight are known
today by only a single copy; eight are known by two copies,
eight by three, and seven by four. Only thirty-one are known by
more than six copies. The number of extant first editions of *Reynard* is therefore relatively high. As a book, the first edition is
quite plain; it would not call for the same pride in ownership and
subsequent care from a bibliophile as would one of Caxton's more

4

elaborate publications. Even though it is not known how many copies usually made up a Caxton edition, the number of copies of the 1481 *Reynard* could well have been low, as low perhaps as one hundred fifty or two hundred. Since, as we shall see, Caxton could not count on an established Reynard tradition among the reading public of England in 1481, he took a financial risk in publishing *Reynard* and consequently must have kept the number of copies down to a minimum. Indeed it is rather mystifying that six copies of an unprepossessing edition that may have had a low number of copies issued were not thumbed to pieces and lost well before modern times.

The book from which Caxton made his translation, usually called the Gouda edition and bearing the simple Middle Dutch title *Die hystorie van Reynaert die Vos*, is a work of considerable literary importance. It is the second printed book of the Reynard story in any language, the Latin *Reinardus Vulpes* of 1473, to be discussed later, being the first. It is the first prose rendering of the verse epic about Reynard and the first printing of any version in the vernacular. It is, finally, the version of Reynard that became an enduring part of popular anonymous chapbook literature in Europe from the sixteenth century down to our own day.

The Gouda edition is a translation into Late Middle Dutch prose of a verse epic written somewhere around 1375. The identity of the man who turned the four-beat couplets of the epic into prose is not known; but whoever he was, he could scarcely have been more illustrious in his field than the book's printer was in his own. To be sure, the verse-to-prose editor and the printer may have been the same man; Caxton himself was printer, editor, and translator all in one. The Dutch printer, however, whose name modern English bibliographers have standardized as Gerard Leeu, seems never to have turned his hand to editorial work. Caxton says in his colophon that he translated his *Reynard the Fox*, though he does not say he printed it. Since he was a well-known printer and since the surviving copies of *Reynard* exhibit type faces peculiarly

5

his, we assume without much question that he did print it. Leeu, on the other hand, says he printed *Die hystorie van Reynaert die Vos;* he does not say he did any editorial work on it. It would be convenient indeed if we could say Leeu saw the manuscript through its editing process from verse to prose, but we cannot. Indirect evidence to the contrary warns us that we should not.

Gerard Leeu's life is simple enough. He was born in 1445, perhaps in Gouda, where at least he lived until 1484; in this year he moved with his printer's equipment to Antwerp and there died in the year 1493. At the age of thirty-two he opened his first printing shop — the one in Gouda — and his first book, conventionally devotional, was called *Epistelen ende ewangelien.* Because of a record saying that in 1484 he made a contribution to the St. Jansgilde of printers and booksellers, we assume that for a short time at least he planned to settle in Bruges, where printing had been progressing since 1474 and where Caxton spent so many years of his life. In September of 1484, however, his first Antwerp publication appeared — *Gemula vocabulorum.* In Antwerp he was successful, being received the year after his arrival in the St. Lucasgilde as a *vrimeester,* one whom the guild had permitted to operate his handicraft independently. His death some eight years later occurred when a typesetter, Henric van Symmen, wanted to set up a press of his own. Leeu opposed him, the two men quarreled, and in the subsequent free-for-all, Leeu was stabbed to death.

Despite absence of any evidence to indicate Leeu ever devoted time and effort to the chores of translation and editing, his reputation as a humanist printer is considerable. In one of his publications that appeared after his death, *Cronycles of the lande of England,* he is praised in the colophon as "an man of grete wysedom in all manner of kunnyng." Erasmus, who knew him, called him a *vir sane lepidus* — "a man of great charm." A check list of his publications is imposing: in the seven years of his stay in Gouda, he produced fifty-eight known publications, among which are various folios; in the nine years of his stay at Antwerp, the total is at least one hundred forty-eight. But two features distinguish

6

Leeu's work from that of other printers of his time: the number of non-Latin works and the number of secular ones. During the Gouda years in particular, Leeu produced numerous popular books whose aim was, despite colophon lip service to their edifying values, chiefly to entertain. To Leeu may be credited eight or nine editions of the famous *Dialogus creaturarum* (in Latin, Netherlandish, and French), three or four editions of Aesop, an edition of the *Historie van Alexander*, and at least one edition of *Reynaert die Vos*. An indication of the strong vernacular tendency of the Gouda years is indicated by the fact that books there produced in Netherlandish total nearly two-thirds of his output while Antwerp saw only something over a fourth appear in the vernacular, the bulk being in Latin.

Caxton left the continent for good in 1476; Leeu's *Reynaert* appeared in 1479, and only two years later Caxton published an English translation of it in London. Although the proximity of these dates might imply some sort of professional association between the two men, other evidence supporting such association is, as we shall see, unimpressive. What these dates do indicate is the surprisingly international character of the book trade in the Low Countries just at this time. Leeu's publications in the last decade of his life bear ample witness to this. Between 1492 and 1493 he published in English *The dyalogus betwixt Salomon and Marcolphus, Thystore of Parys and Vyenne, The history of Iason*, and the *Cronycles of the lande of England*. These four books, produced in the first two years after Caxton's death, established Leeu as the first Netherlandish printer to publish English works; but such publication does not point to any particular association with England beyond that which commercial enterprise would occasion. Such enterprise was behind Leeu's publication in French of the ever popular *Dialogus creaturarum*, for Leeu was also the first Netherlandish printer to publish French works. That *Reynaert die Vos* fell into Caxton's hands when it did may simply be the result of Leeu's energy and diverse activities as a printer.

The final paragraph of the Gouda edition reads: *Hier eyndet die hystorie van reynaert die vos ende is gheprent ter goude in hollant by mi gheraert leeu den seventienden dach in augusto. Int iaer M.CCCC. ende lxxix* (Here ends the history of Reynard the Fox and was printed at Gouda in Holland by me Gerard Leeu the seventeenth day in August in the year 1479). How well the work was received on its publication is difficult to say, except that Leeu must have taken far less of a risk than Caxton since Reynard was far more familiar in Low German lands than he was in England. No evidence exists that Leeu produced a second edition in Gouda, although a Delft edition of 1485 exists. In the Delft edition no printer's name is given, but presumably the printer was Jacob Jacobszoon van der Meer, to whom are ascribed three other works originally published by Leeu. Both the Gouda and the Delft editions correspond page for page and line for line as far as leaf 69; from leaf 70 the Delft edition contains two or three more lines per page than does the Gouda; then, toward the end, parallel correspondence resumes. Even if Leeu may not have been the printer of the Delft edition, the Gouda edition undoubtedly was its original and it can be considered a second edition. In one respect the Delft edition is enormously important; it served as the original of the Antwerp *volksboek* of 1564, which became a huge success as popular literature and spread throughout Europe in succeeding centuries as did very few other works of its kind.

Of the two surviving copies of the Gouda edition, one is in the British Museum and the other in the Koninklyke Bibliotheek in The Hague. *The British Museum Catalogue of Printed Books 1881–1900* describes the former:

Without title page or catchwords. 111 leaves of text numbered at the foot, making with the two unmarked leaves of table 113 in all. 27 lines to a full page. The numeration of the leaves makes only 110, but the no. 70 occurs twice. Sig[natures] *a–o*. The earliest edition [of the prose version of Reynard] in any language.

Caxton's *Reynard*, which is the second earliest edition of the prose version of Reynard, is very similar in physical make-up. It has no title page, no catchwords, and no pagination. Signatures run from

8

Dit is die tafel van deſen boecke dartmen
hiet die hyſtozie vã reynaert die vos

Table of Contents of the Gouda edition of 1479

a to *l*, all in eights except *k* and *l*, which have but six leaves each. Caxton's edition also exhibits inconsistencies rarely seen in modern books. The leaf preceding signature i_1 is printed only halfway down on either side; what should be Chapter XXVIII is left unnumbered; two chapters bear the number forty-three; the table of contents overlooks the unnumbered chapter and lists only the second of the two chapters bearing the same number. Caxton's edition totals but eighty-five leaves of text to the one hundred eleven leaves of Leeu's. This discrepancy is not due to deletions on Caxton's part or to any brevity of the English language vis-à-vis Middle Dutch, but to the fact that Caxton's page averages twenty-nine lines while Leeu's averages twenty-seven and that Caxton's line averages eleven words while Leeu's averages nine and often less. Neither text contains illustrations; both are bare of superfluous decoration, although the Dutch work has a few rubricated capital letters.

E. G. Duff in *The Cambridge History of English Literature*, when discussing Caxton's *Reynard*, says it was "apparently" translated from a prose version which appeared in Gouda, Holland, in 1479. His qualification would imply that some doubt exists as to whether the Gouda book was really seen, handled, and translated by Caxton. A careful line by line comparison of the English and Middle Dutch texts shows that the one commits errors where the other does also, that Caxton deviates only where the Gouda text is faulty, that where the Gouda text is outright nonsense Caxton's text is also nonsense or tries to cover a blunder by replacing nonsense with something reasonably intelligible. Caxton, in other words, must have used the Gouda text as we have it today. Making this statement, which the textual annotations of the present edition bear out, is necessary since vague suppositions that Caxton's original has yet to be found appear here and there in critical literature. Such suppositions were sired in 1877 by William Blades in his *The Biography and Typography of William Caxton*, still a standard work after almost three-quarters of a century. Blades had heard of the discovery of the so-called "Culemann

Fragments" (now called the "Cambridge Fragments") in 1854 by Senator F. G. H. Culemann of Hannover. These fragments in small quarto of a late fifteenth century Reynard in verse are important in that they are the immediate source of the Middle Low German *Reinke de Vos*, printed in Lübeck in 1498, and that their glosses appear in the chapbook *Reynard de Vos* published in Antwerp in 1564. Unfortunately Blades suggested that these fragments might also be a source of Caxton's *Reynard*. Had Blades really looked into the matter, he would have found that the fragments were published some six years after Caxton's edition of *Reynard*.

J. W. Muller and Henri Logeman, who in 1892 published the only modern annotated edition of the Gouda text, summarize its general literary quality (translation mine):

> The prose edition may scarcely bear the name of a reworking. It follows the text of *Reinaert II* [the verse original, *Reinaerts Historie*] ploddingly — indeed it is for the most part nothing other than the text with somewhat altered syntax and with only partial omission of rhyme words, which often enough come out in the prose. The style is on the whole rather flowing, although the structure of sentences is often fairly clumsy; anacolutha, constructions *apo koinou*, and the like appear often. Much of this one may attribute to extremely careless printing, yet much also is . . . proper to Middle Dutch which at the time still lay in its swaddling clothes . . . . We have here to do, moreover, with a chapbook, on which certainly neither scribe nor printer would expend the care he would on a more important or more sizable folio and quarto.

Muller and Logeman neglect to add that the same criticism, both favorable and unfavorable, may also be applied to Caxton's translation and its printing.

Just who turned the verse of *Reinaerts Historie* into prose is not known, but, as we have seen, it probably was not Gerard Leeu, although he may have delegated the work of transcription from verse to prose to a scribe or lay monk. Such a practice was at the time not uncommon. There is, of course, the possibility that a prose Reynard had circulated in manuscript before 1479 and that Leeu merely printed an opportune copy. Even though the verse original is usually dated more than a century prior to the printing of the Gouda edition, versions of Reynard in prose and verse may have been quite numerous and eagerly read, for the spate of printed versions within nineteen years before the turn of the sixteenth century — one in Middle Dutch prose, one in Middle Dutch verse, one in English prose, and one in Middle Low German — bespeaks anything but neglect. Yet the prose version used by Leeu may indeed have been relatively new in 1479: its printed copy contains not only the usual typographic errors and blunders, but also numerous senseless textual defects which time and repeated scribal transcription would have tended to wear away. We may even discern in various indirect ways the personality of the man who wrote out Leeu's original.

The prose redactor apparently had a scholarly background, for he occasionally corrected tags of Latin in the verse original. With proverbs he could not leave well enough alone; often he replaced the one he found with one of his own or allowed the proverb he found to stand only after adding explanatory material. In place of "For right often has need of help" he substitutes "For blood must creep where it cannot walk." "I'm no bird to entice with chaff" he elaborates into "I'm no bird whom one may entice with chaff — I know my barley." Muller and Logeman suspect that the redactor of the prose version, lay monk though he might have been, elaborated certain indecorous passages "not seldom with noticeable pleasure"; they list no less than seven that apparently aroused their concern in 1892. A sober check of the seven today reveals that the elaboration is very minor indeed. Quite in his favor is the fact that the prose redactor does not expand moralizing passages, of which there are many in the second part of his original. It is possible that a very badly preserved or much used manuscript was employed as *Vorlage*, for very often in the prose there appear words of different meaning from but of similar appearance to corresponding words in the original: *oren* (ears) is given where *oghen* (eyes) is meant, *fyn* (fine) for *syn* (his), and so on. Actual omissions in the prose version are few and minor for a work of such length; Muller and Logeman list but twenty-five, most of which are explainable by the fact that the prose redactor in or near 1479 quite naturally failed to understand certain phrases and words in a work written down a hundred years before. Lines 5486–5489 of the original, for example, read "the bone is polished just as bright as if it were of fine silver, thereto as white as if it might be of ivory or bocraen." The prose rendering stops with "of fine silver"; the word *bocraen*, meaning a fabric of some sort (glosses variously say it is silken, hempen, or of goat's hair), puzzled him and he omitted it and the phrase containing it. Such omissions point more to a lack of an adequate reference library than to carelessness or a desire to improve on the style of the original. In short, the man who turned Reynard into prose, followed his original, as did Caxton, as near as he reasonably could.

Muller and Logeman feel that they can localize the prose redactor by his choice of language. He shows a tendency, they feel, to prefer northern Middle Dutch forms over southern, and Gouda is linguistically in the northern area. Also, where the verse original reads *ic hebbe ghehoort noemen Aken. Parijs Kolen ende Duwa* (I've heard named Aachen, Paris, Cologne, and Douai), the prose reads "*zyricxzee*" for "*Duwa*." Muller and Logeman feel that here they have the home of the prose redactor: in Zierikzee on the island of Schouwen in Zeeland in the northern language area. These indications of northern origin are important in that they offer the only evidence of affinity between the northern printer and the poor drudge who turned 7794 lines of verse into fairly readable prose.

13

CHAPTER II

THE RISE OF REYNARD
IN THE LOW COUNTRIES

THE prose redactor of the Gouda edition was conservative. His major contributions to Reynard consist in the division of the story into forty-five chapters and the addition of clauses at each chapter break summarizing the content of the chapter.

The two verse epics — the earlier *Van den Vos Reinaerde*, hereafter called *Reinaert I*, and its enlargement and continuation *Reinaerts Historie*, hereafter called *Reinaert II* — contain no chapter headings and no summarizing clauses. They belong to periods that could do without such things, but they do contain large colored initials situated throughout their texts, each usually signaling a turn in plot. Comparing the colored initials of *Reinaert II* with the chapter breaks in the Gouda edition reveals just how conservative the prose redactor was. Thirty-two of his chapter breaks occur exactly where a colored initial appears in *Reinaert II*.

The verse epic *Reinaert II* has survived complete in only one manuscript, now called the Brussels Manuscript and kept as number 14601 in the Royal Library in The Hague. It came to light in 1836 at a sale in Amsterdam. Little is known of its prior history beyond the fact that in the sixteenth century two women, Margriet, daughter of Jan Beyer, and Marya van Ham, daughter of Haeyndrick van Bijler, wrote their names on the flyleaf. The manuscript contains one hundred twenty leaves in folio with thirty-four lines per side. Originally there must have been five miniatures pasted into the manuscript, since removed or lost. Paleographers have assumed that it was written in the first third of the fifteenth century. Only the name of the scribe, Claes van Aken, is certain. He added an envoy of twelve lines that contains

his name twice. If the letters ending the twelve lines are read upward, *claesuanaken* appears; the name again appears if the letters
ending the words in the middle of the lines are read upward.
Reinaert II received its first fully annotated edition in 1836 from
Jan-Frans Willems, a Flemish nationalist poet, and its best from
Ernst Martin in 1874. A fragmentary manuscript of *Reinaert II*
exists, which is called the Van Wijn Manuscript after the name
of the man who discovered it in 1800. It begins at line 6755 of the
Brussels Manuscript, the place where Isegrim and Reynard de-
cide to settle their differences by personal combat, and runs with-
out break to the end. It is written out on paper — the Brussels
Manuscript is on parchment — and bears the date 1477. Jacob
Grimm published the Van Wijn Manuscript in 1834 in his book
Reinhart Fuchs, the work which gave impetus to modern Reynard
scholarship, two years before the complete version came to light
in the form of the Brussels Manuscript.

    Reinaert II, which the poet himself calls *Reinaerts Historie* in
the next to the last line, was composed by a person whose identity
is unknown. He took up *Van den Vos Reinaerde (Reinaert I)* a
decade or two before 1400 and altered it only in minor ways and
then added a continuation that in plot and length duplicates the
first part. The astonishing thing about the finished product is
that a casual reader may not immediately detect how very much
the second part is indebted to the first. Although medievalists and
literary historians assume that it is inferior to *Reinaert I*, unfavorable professional criticism of *Reinaert II* should be questioned.
Goethe's *Reineke Fuchs* of 1794 is more often than not considered
the best of Reynard treatments — perhaps because it is the work
of a very great poet — and yet Goethe's version is in the form
which the *Reinaert II* poet gave the Reynard story. The Lübeck
edition of 1498, the version Goethe used for his *Reineke Fuchs*
via Gottsched's 1752 translation of it into High German, is a mere
translation into Low German of Henric van Alcmaer's recopying
of *Reinaert II*, which Henric completed around 1487. The Lübeck
edition, whose Low German title is *Reinke de Vos*, shows few

15

divergencies from *Reinaert II*, perhaps an additional earthy turn of phrase here and an extra moralistic flourish there, but little more. Just as it does with Goethe's *Reineke Fuchs*, professional criticism treats the Lübeck edition very well: nowhere does it heavy-handedly praise the first part and belittle the second.

The truth of the matter is that the judgments made against *Reinaert II* are academic. They are made by and primarily for medievalists. The average reader may not even notice the split in the Reynard story; certainly it is far less pronounced than in such medieval pieces as the *Nibelungenlied* and the *Chancon de Roland*. Caxton himself may not have noticed it, for the transition is natural. Noble the king learns of Reynard's failure to go on a pilgrimage when Bellin delivers the head of the hare Cuwart in Reynard's pilgrim's bag; Noble releases Bruin and Isegrim from prison and holds a feast to placate them. Here, as in the beginning, messengers appear bearing news of further transgressions on Reynard's part. This is all very natural. Reynard is at large and no worse and no better than he ever was. Well into the second part one might begin to notice that there are more digressions than in the first, such as the fable that tells of the price of a foal being inscribed on the hoof of a mare or the long description of the wondrous mirror of antiquity. These digressions are entertaining in their way and also, since some of them are put in the mouth of the arch rogue himself, highly ironic. Although professional judgments leveled against the second part of *Reinaert II* matter little to the average reader's enjoyment of the book, they do point out certain important stylistic features.

Jacob Wijbrand Muller, the most prominent of modern Dutch Reynard scholars, gave in 1884 a full account of the medievalist's case against *Reinaert II* in his extensive work *De oude en de jongere bewerking van den Reinaert*. His views, judging by their repetition in standard literary histories, have become orthodox. Muller begins by saying that the *Reinaert II* poet was not an "original creative artist of genius" since he invents little, follows his predecessor — or perhaps predecessors — in the first part and

16

adopts a series of fragments from the earlier *Roman de Renart* and from classical fabulists in the second. He does not, according to Muller, arrange his components into a balanced narrative — namely, into an epic with a neat rounding off of motives and a beginning and end without extraneous intervening matter, although he perhaps tried. Such comment is in part valid, except that it overlooks how stunningly the *Reinaert II* poet topped off his work with the mock-heroic combat between Isegrim and Reynard.

More perceptive is Muller's view that the *Reinaert II* poet approaches his material from a point of view totally different from that of his predecessor. While the older poet seems to take an objective uncritical delight in his hero, the younger very often uses Reynard as an evil example on which to base moralizations. Muller plays heavily on the idea that a polarity exists between a naive artist and a conscious one. Quite in accord with the spirit of Schiller's *Über naive und sentimentalische Dichtung*, he and his followers would have us understand that the *Reinaert II* poet is disappointingly *sentimentalisch* and hence allows his narrative to become subordinate to doctrine, moral, and satire. To be sure, the old objective verve is not completely present in *Reinaert II*, but rarely does a reader get the impression that the poet goes before his public to reason, criticize, and preach.

The medievalists are not totally one-sided; their criticism encompasses some praise, albeit faint. They do, for example, say that the *Reinaert II* poet can on occasion improve on the verse technique of his source — a point that should, however, be taken somewhat cautiously, for where the manuscripts of *Reinaert I* show occasional clumsiness, one cannot always be certain whether such should be attributed to the poet or to a scribe. Most of the medievalists agree in saying that the *Reinaert II* poet was a *Menschenkenner*, a man who knew and challenged the evils of his time and contemporaries.

What such criticism leaves unsaid is that it is a wonder the *Reinaert II* poet performed as well as he did. The *Reinaert I* poet,

17

or poets, did after all use somewhat coherent sections of the French *Roman de Renart*, and these the continuator merely duplicated — of course with the omission of the Bruin and Tibert incidents and with the addition of the combat between Reynard and Isegrim, itself taken from the *Roman*.

The prologue to *Reinaert II* (forty-four lines) as well as its slightly shorter original in *Reinaert I* (forty lines) is defensive and apologetic. In the former, a certain Willem says that it grieved him to see the adventures of Reynard remain without transcription into the German language and that he in consequence rendered Reynard's life into "German" by using the proper French books. (His "German" is what we today would call late Middle Dutch.) He says that he has in mind fools and boors who cannot appreciate his rhymes and who should therefore let them stand uncriticized. He adds that he wrote his poem at the request of a lady *die in grooter heuscheden / gherne keert al haer saken* (who in great propriety takes care of her affairs). He says finally that he wishes neither boor nor fool to read his work but only serious individuals "who take pains to foster courtesy and turn their minds to courteous conduct."

That the second part of *Reinaert II* and hence all related versions, including Caxton's, roughly approximate the first is due not only to the lack of independent invention on the part of the *Reinaert II* poet, but also to the fact that he chose as the general framework of his second part a *branche* of the *Roman de Renart* that is roughly similar to the one used by the *Reinaert I* poet — namely, *branche* VI in Martin's edition or *branche* 20 in Méon's. Here Reynard is found to have committed gross crimes against Isegrim, Tibert, Bruin, and other animals of lesser consequence and even against Noble the lion and his queen. Reynard appears, requesting acquittal either by God's judgment or trial by combat. The latter is decided upon and the stag Brichemer is assigned as judge and the leopard, the boar, and the bull chosen as seconds. Isegrim is victorious and Reynard, condemned to death, stalls his execution with a long confession. Rescued by a passing monk, he is taken to a monastery where the sight of the capons purchased by the brothers quickly turns his mind to theft and away from righteous conduct. He is expelled from the order and is happy to be free again. What there is in the second part of *Reinaert II* that cannot be traced to the sixth *branche* of the *Roman de Renart* comes from fable literature, chivalric romance, Physiologus, and tags of classical antiquity which were the common property of medieval scholars.

It is not surprising at all that little has been written about *Reinaert II*, for although the poet remains completely anonymous, the source of his continuation of *Reinaert I* and his incidental elaborations are obvious. Reynard scholarship really begins — one can say it almost ends — with the older vernacular epic. Since 1811, when Ferdinand Weckerlin first called scholarly attention to *Van den Vos Reinaerde (Reinaert I)*, western European scholars have expended enormous effort in attempting to date it, restore the original text from several widely divergent manuscripts, and ascertain just where the credit for creating the comic beast epic should be assigned. So much of this scholarship is so purely polemical that it is best to begin with the very simplest of facts.

Reinaert I survives in only two relatively complete manuscripts. One is the Comburg Manuscript (3469 lines), now in the Württembergische Landesbibliothek in Stuttgart. It was copied sometime in the first half of the fourteenth century and first edited by F. D. Gräter in 1812. The other is the Dyck Manuscript (3393 lines), now in Schloss Alfter near Bonn. It was discovered in 1907, first described by Herman Degering, and gave rise to the Arnout-Perrot controversy. This manuscript was also copied sometime in the first half of the fourteenth century, although paleographers assume it to be somewhat older than the Comburg Manuscript. Two fragmentary and mutilated manuscripts exist: the Rotterdam Fragments, now in the Gemeende-Bibliotheek in Rotterdam, and the Darmstadt Fragments, now in the Hessische Landesbibliothek in Darmstadt. By the use of all known manuscripts — the fragmentary as well as the relatively complete ones — plus considerable outright emendation modern editors are able to produce a smooth and readable version of *Reinaert I*. All manuscripts were presumably transcribed over a hundred years after *Reinaert I* was set down in its original form, and it is rare indeed that even one line appears the same in all manuscripts. The most widely used and respected text of *Reinaert I*, that edited by J. W. Muller, is actually a synthesis. It departs repeatedly page after page from any one of the existing manuscripts in its orthography, word order, and line meaning. Muller's intention is for his text to represent *Reinaert I* as it was set down by the poet himself and as it no longer exists today.

The prologue to *Reinaert I* says in forty lines essentially what the *Reinaert II* prologue says in forty-four. But since the earlier epic, which was written sometime before 1272, also mentions Willem, it would seem that Willem did not write *Reinaert II*, but *Reinaert I*. He must be the individual whose comic genius retold the first *branche* of the *Roman de Renart* (according to Martin's edition or the twentieth *branche* according to Méon's), capped it with the supposed conspiracy against Nobel the lion — his own invention — and thereby created a masterwork that Dutch and Flemish critics do not hesitate to place beside the greatest literary masterpieces of world literature. The little epic has suffered immeasurably by being written in a literary language and by being part of a national literature which is out of the general swim of Western culture; but there is nothing in other literatures that is quite like it: to discover it and to become familiar with it, although not necessarily with the historical and philological problems that beset it, is a delight that can be equaled by few other works stemming from the same period.

Undoubtedly the most important evidence concerning the authorship of *Reinaert I* is in the first ten lines of the prologue in the Dyck Manuscript. It runs in diplomatic form but with scribal abbreviations written out:

> VVillam die madock makede
> Daer hi dicke omme wakede
> Hem vernoyde so harde

Villam die madocke makede
Daer hi dicke omme wakede
Hi ne vonde so harde
Dat ene auenture van rynaerde
In dietsche was onvolmaket bleuen
Die arnout niet en hadde vescreuen
Dat hi die vite dede soeken
En hise uten walsche boeken
In dietsche heuet begonnen
God moete hem sire hulpe onnen
Nv keert hem dar toe mijn sin
Dat ic bidde mdhr begin
Dese de dorpers en ten doren
Of si comen dar si horen
Dese rime en dese woert
Dien si onuutte sijn gehoert
Dat sise laten onbescauen
Te vele slachte si den rauen
Die emer es al cume malsch
Si make sulke rime valsch
Daer si niet meer af ne weten
Dan ic doe hoe die gene heten
Die nv in babilonie leuen
Dat si wel si souden begeuen
Mijns dichtens waer oer gestille
Dat ne doegic niet dur hare wille
En hads mi niet gebeten
Die mi groter houescheten
Herne keret hare saken
Si bad mi dat ic soude maken
Dese auenture van reynaerde
A Uwegrepent die gruncte
Ic wil wel dat se te gode hore
En daer toe geue haer oren
Die gaerne plegen der heren
Si hare sin daer toe keren
Dat si arme sijn sieke.

Verses 1-37 of the Dyck Manuscript of *Van den Vos Reinaerde*

Dater ene auenture van reynaerde
Jn dietsche was onvolmaket bleuen
Die arnout niet en hadde bescreuen
Dat hi die vite dede soeken
Ende hise vten walschen boeken
Jn dietsche hevet begonnen
God moete hem sire hulpen onnen

Willem, who wrote Madoc [probably a romance, now no longer extant], over which he often stayed awake, was so much perturbed that an adventure of Reynard remained without complete transcription into *dietsch* [Middle Dutch], which Arnout had not written out, that he attempted the adventure [more accurately "the biography"] and began it in *dietsch* out of French books. May God grant him his help.

Simple as it seems, this passage can be and has been variously interpreted. The court of Noble the lion, the hearing of Reynard's transgressions, and the Tibert and Bruin incidents are from the *Roman*. Reynard's great lie about the conspiracy against Noble is the invention of the Middle Dutch poet. Consequently, it must have been the second part that Arnout composed and the first part, since it does come from "French books," that Willem began in *dietsch*. However strange it appears to assume an early poet wrote the second part of an epic and a later one the first, responsible editors have accepted such a notion. Other editors, since the very last incident — Reynard's proposed pilgrimage — does have its counterpart in the *Roman*, have assumed that the poet refers to this *inter alia* when he mentions "French books" and that therefore Arnout could very well have written the first and hence older part and Willem the second.

Overlooking for a moment the names Arnout and Willem, we should note that as early as 1897 Leonard Willems suggested that *Reinaert I* was not only made up of two parts each of different origin, but also composed by two different poets. In 1907 when the Dyck Manuscript appeared — the only one in which the name Arnout appears — the psychological assurance given to those who dissect a literary work and assign individual authorship to separate sections must have been tremendous. The conservative multiple authorship view now maintains that the break in *Reinaert I* occurs where Reynard appears in court and is condemned to be hanged. The extreme view is that of J. W. Muller, the most sophisticated of Reynard scholars and the most formidable of the multiple authorship proponents. He assumes that the first part comprises lines 41 to 1900 (in his own particular edition of *Reinaert I*) and the second, lines 1 to 40 and 1901 to the end. He suggests that a third (anonymous) poet revised the original by Arnout-Willem and inserted, among other things, Reynard's long confession of his sins to Grimbert; that a fourth (anonymous) poet added most of the lines following verse 3360, and that a fifth (anonymous) poet added the terminal lines that contain Willem's name in an acrostic. Muller's thesis rests on very learned phonological, historical, and stylistic inferences; if one accepts them, his thesis involving five poets is inevitable; if one does not, his thesis is absurd.

A much simpler approach to the problem of authorship is that which assumes the *Arnout* of the Dyck Manuscript to be a scribal error for *Perrot*, an Old French form of Pierre de St. Cloud, the man who wrote a good number of beast *fabliaux* in the *Roman de Renart*. The scribal-error theory, arbitrary as it seems at first, is made plausible when the first ten lines of the first *branche* of the *Roman* are considered. They appear in the Roques edition:

> Perroz, qui son engin ess' art
> mist en vers faire de Renart
> ed d'Isengrin son chier compere,
> laissa le mieuz de sa matiere
> quant il entroblia les paiz
> et le jugement qui fu faiz,
> en la cort Noble le lion,
> de la grant fornicacion
> que Renart fist, qui toz max cove,
> envers dame Hersent la love.

Perroz, who put his talent and his art into making verse about Reynard and Isegrim, his dear companion, left the best of his material when he forgot the suits and the judgment which was rendered at the court of Noble the lion of the great fornication that Reynard, who secretly prepares all harmful acts, did upon lady Hersent the she-wolf.

In the *Reinaert I* prologue the poet refers to the man who failed to complete the poem (Arnout) and to himself (Willem) — in the third person, to be sure, but this is not uncommon in medieval works — while in the *Roman* prologue the poet does not give his own name, only that of the man who failed to complete the poem (Perroz), but the general statement of the two prologues is the same — "here begins the work that someone else failed to complete." Moreover, the first *branche* of the *Roman*, although perhaps in a version earlier than the one that has come down to us, is the source of the first part of *Reinaert I*. Approached from this point of view, the *Reinaert I* prologue is merely Willem's paraphrase of the *Roman* prologue.

But what of "Arnout"? If he is not just a scribal error, all that can be said of him is that he exists only in the sixth line of the Dyck Manuscript. He still provokes theories concerning his existence: Wytze Gs Hellinga, the editor of the great multiple-text edition of all Middle Dutch Reynard epics, now believes that "Arnout" was a cuckold and did not want to complete a poem about a cuckold — Isegrim, the fox's arch enemy, being the cuckold in question here. The view that *Reinaert I* is the work of one poet is, moreover, gaining ground. This development seems sensible. The major break in the poem is inevitable: it occurs where Reynard is condemned to be hanged, the spot where the *Roman* source ends. What, then, of the apparent changes in narrative technique that appear after the break, such as the one most commonly mentioned, the change whereby the animals seem to assume a greater variety of human traits? The change of subject matter would seem to be the explanation. Finally, what of the philological evidence indicating multiple authorship that J. W. Muller has so carefully compiled? Jan van Mierlo, whose stature as a Reynard scholar is now no less than Muller's, remarks in his section of *De letterkunde van de Middeleeuwen* that "the copyists have so freely made changes, bun-

24

gled, and made additions . . . that scarcely anything can be inferred from them." Van Mierlo's point may be illustrated by the last lines of the Comburg Manuscript, those wherein the "Willem" acrostic appears. The lines read in diplomatic transcription but with scribal abbreviations written out:

> Bi gode ic dart hu wel raden
> Isengrijn sprac toten beere
> Wat sechdire to brune heere
> Brune sprach ic hebbe lieure in de rijsere
> Dan hier to ligghene int ysere
> Laet ons toten coninc gaen
> Ende sinen pays daer ontfaen
> Met syrapeel datse ghinghen
> Ende maecten pays van allen dinghen

"By God, I dare counsel you that well." [These are the last words of Firapel the leopard, who advises the prisoners, Bruin and Isegrim, to come to terms with the king.] Isegrim spoke to the bear: "What do you say to that, Sir Bruin?" Bruin said, "I'd rather lie in the brush than here in irons. Let us go to the king and accept his peace." Thereupon they went with Syrapeel [an error for Firapeel] and made peace in all things.

The fourth and fifth lines of the above (in J. W. Muller's emendation) once must have read something like this:

> ic laghe sprac Brune in den risern
> liever dan hier in den iseren

for so written out, the nine lines, if their first letters are read downward, present the signature *bi willeme* (by Willem). Even though the probably older Dyck Manuscript does not contain the acrostic and hence it is likely that the *Reinaert I* poet did not compose the acrostic, its presence in the Comburg Manuscript may be construed — and is so construed by the proponents of single authorship — as scribal tribute to an enduring literary reputation, that of "Willem who wrote Madoc."

Both Muller and van Mierlo would have *Reinaert I* written sometime before 1200. Wise supposition alone supports this date.

Actually we can only say that *Reinaert I* was written before 1272, a date derived from a Latin translation of *Reinaert I* called *Reinardus Vulpes* done by Baldwin the Young (*Balduinus iuvenis*), which he dedicated to the Dean of Bruges, Jan van Dampierre,

Incipit reynardus vulpes feliciter

Abula reynardi
ficut reoz agnita multis
Teutonice fcripta
metrificata fonet
Affit principio nature fuma poteftas
Tocius mufe fons et origo boni
Brugis prepofite cui nobilitatis origa
Nomen liorici peruenit vfqz ducis
Primꝰ flandrefis fuit hic comes hoeqz creati
Sunt reges.comites.funt quoqz.funtqz duces
At proauus cefar conftantino politanus
Flandrenfis qz comes bānonie qz fuit
Ac princeps auia cui nobilitate feða

The beginning of the Latin *Reynardus Vulpes*

whom chronicles list as being dean from 1269 to 1272. That a vernacular work should be translated at this time into Latin is a singular honor. Baldwin, moreover, did not set about the task merely to exercise his Latin: he carefully rounded off the epic with an etiological flourish. Bellin the ram is saved from Bruin and

Isegrim by human beings on the condition that he give them his wool each year; Tibert the cat's sufferings are compensated for by his being allowed to live at ease in human dwellings and catch mice; Reynard gets his just deserts by being proclaimed an outlaw for all time. *Reinardus* exists in one copy today, an incunabulum printed in Utrecht in 1473 and now in the Athenaeum Bibliotheek in Deventer, Holland, a fact, sometimes overlooked by historians of the Flemish vernacular epics, which makes it the oldest printing of a Reynard work in existence. M. F. A. G. Campbell put out a diplomatic edition of it in 1859 and since that time editors have used it as a guide in restoring thirteenth century readings to the fourteenth century manuscripts of *Reinaert I*.

With *Reinaert I* the path of descent, which may be traced back in time from Caxton's *Reynard*, becomes indistinct. To be sure, the first *branche* of the *Roman de Renart*, which may be a generation or more earlier, is very close to *Reinaert I*, but only up to the conspiracy scene. Anyone reading the individual *branches* of the *Roman* after reading *Reinaert I* misses a certain integration of incident and a definite beginning and ending. The *Roman* arose in time alongside the *fabliaux*, and the various branches of the *Roman* present series of *fabliaux* using animals and not human beings as protagonists. The *Roman* incidents remained animal *fabliaux* even though a scribe often set himself to gather them and write them down. Each *branche* is a motley of several tales held together usually by continuity of subject matter. No definite canon of *Roman branches* has been universally agreed upon, chiefly because of the great number of individual manuscripts and the great number of different versions of similar tales. There is, however, in the *Roman* one relatively well-integrated series of tales, which is one of the oldest. It is usually dated in the latter part of the twelfth century and is the only series that shows epic characteristics. This series makes up *branche I* and served as the chief source and inspiration of the *Reinaert I* poet.

The existence of an epic impulse in a given people has been a matter of much controversy, often of the most nationalistic and ungenial kind. The Greeks had it, and some historians assert that the French are lacking it (the *Chançon de Roland* they explain away as being essentially Germanic) and that the English and Germans are possessed of it. The question is delicate. It is best here to offer evidence and see to what conclusions it leads. Before *Reinaert I* there appeared three quasi-beast epics, *Reinhart Fuchs*, *Ysengrimus*, and *Ecbasis captivi*. The first is in Middle High German, written in its original form around 1182 by a certain Heinrich, presumably an Alsatian. The second, in Latin, was written very close to 1150 by Master Nivardus of Ghent. The third, also in Latin, was written according to general scholarly assumption, around 940 by a monk of German origin in a monastery in Toul in northeastern France. All these can be and have been called "Germanic" despite their Romance background and all presage the appearance of *Van den Vos Reinaerde*, the beast epic in its most artistically mature form.

Reinhart Fuchs or, to use the title now favored by editors, *Fuchs Reinhart* is preserved in its oldest version in fragmentary form in one manuscript, now in the Landesbibliothek in Kassel and in a later complete version in two manuscripts, one in the Universitäts-Bibliothek in Heidelberg and the other in the Metropolitanbibliothek in Kolocsa, Hungary. Complete it runs to 2265 lines, about two-thirds the length of *Reinaert I*. As a literary piece to be enjoyed, it is rather poor, although Georg Baesecke did a readable modern German version of it in 1926 that does much to cover up the abrupt transitions and episodic nature of the original. The point here is that it presents as a literary achievement nothing more than what the *Roman* presents and in a more or less polished manner. Even though it does contain the Bruin and Tibert incidents, it is closer to the *Roman* than to *Reinaert I* and much of the scholarship relating to it centers on the question of whether or not it may be derived from — even translated from — a *branche* of the *Roman* that predates any of the existing *branches*.

28

Written a good quarter century before *Reinhart Fuchs* and perhaps less than a half century before *Reinaert I*, and in Flanders, the 6574 lines of *Ysengrimus* make up a work that in narrative progression corresponds to an epic. The tone, however, is didactic and the animal characters decidedly human in their make-up, two features absent in *Reinaert I*. Only two editions of it have appeared, one in 1832 by F. J. Mone and another in 1884 by Ernst Voigt, although a somewhat crabbed modern German translation by Albert Schönfelder (1955) and a study by Jan van Mierlo (1943) indicate that it may finally receive the attention it deserves. The hero is Isegrim, not Reynard, and his misfortunes are related in seven well-rounded books, the whole ending with the death of the wolf. The animals are given proper names, but whether for the first time in a literary work is a matter of debate, since it is impossible to prove whether *Ysengrimus* came before or after the *Roman fabliaux*. Certain incidents are common to *Ysengrimus* and the *Roman*, but no extant *branche* of the *Roman* may be pointed to as the source of the former. Significant is the fact that some of the incidents in *Ysengrimus* are, as are the Bruin and Tibert incidents in Caxton's *Reynard* and in the Flemish vernacular epics, descended ultimately not from classic fable but from the animal tale of Western European folklore. Jacob Grimm and many contemporary folklorists assume that these are the building blocks of the beast epic: these and not Aesopic fables lend themselves well to linkage and to the development of an epic narrative. *Ysengrimus* could have appeared in those sections of northern France, as Picardy, Normandy, and the Isle de France, where the *Roman fabliaux* were at home. Dutch and Flemish scholars, not without considerable pride, point out that *Ysengrimus*, the first long beast narrative with an epic ring, appeared where one should expect it to appear — namely, in Flanders.

Just how one should classify *Ecbasis captivi* (The Production of the Idle Hours of a Captive) is difficult to say, but the label "epic" clings to it in most literary histories. Given one edition in 1874 by Ernst Voigt, it consists of 1175 rhymed hexameters and structurally it presents a fable within a fable. The monk who wrote it ran away from the strict discipline of his order and was ultimately captured and imprisoned. He wrote *Ecbasis* as an allegorical representation of his own plight. The outer fable tells of a calf's escape from its stall and its subsequent rescue from the wolf. The inner fable, told by the wolf during the time his lair is besieged, concerns the healing of the sick lion by the use of a wolf's pelt. The whole ends with the victory of the besiegers and the death of the wolf. To be sure, the animals are not given names and the incidents smack of Aesopic didacticism, but *Ecbasis* does represent the first real attempt at a long animal tale in verse in all of modern Western European literature.

CHAPTER III

WILLIAM CAXTON'S DISCOVERY OF REYNARD THE FOX

THERE is not a little that is paradoxical about Caxton and his career. He is England's first printer, but his first publications appeared on the Continent. His printing techniques most probably were learned in Cologne and, although he apparently never visited France, some of his first books were in French. If Malory had not written about King Arthur, Caxton would be the chief literary figure of fifteenth century England, yet he wrote little beyond a handful of self-effacing prologues and epilogues. In contrast to some early printers, he made publishing a paying proposition, for very few of his works appeared without patronage or without a ready demand on the part of the book-buying public, but when he produced on his own, when he printed works not under the safeguard of patronage and not aimed at satisfying a public need, he chose to print the finest humanistic pieces available in his day. This he did not have to do: this fact should rank him as the earliest and one of the best of English literary critics.

Caxton's biographers say that he spent thirty-odd years in the Low Countries and add that the probable years of arrival and departure were 1441 and 1476. The first year is easily come by. In the Prologue to the first book printed in English, *The Recuyell of the Historyes of Troye*, Caxton writes that he began translating "to eschewe slouthe and ydleness" from a book "drawn in the frenche," but did so brashly since he "began . . . to renne forth as blynde bayard" (a brash steed taken as the epitome of recklessness). He says that he soon became aware of his own "sympleness and unperfightness" and confesses:

In france was I never and was born and learned myn englissh in kent

31

in the weeld where I doubte not is spoken as brode and rude english as in ony place of englond and have contynued by the space of .xxx. year for the most part in the countries of Braband, flanders, holand, and zeland.

This reference, to be sure, is not the only evidence of Caxton's Low German excursion; for in addition to the knowledge of Dutch admitted in the *Prologue to Reynard the Fox*, a score or so of official records from the last quarter of the fifteenth century indicate that a William Caxton lived in the Low Countries first in the service of the Merchant Adventurers, a group of English businessmen belonging to a sort of international clearing house, and later in the service of the English king.

Since the Prologue to *The Recuyell* was written in 1471, Caxton must have been in the Low Countries by 1441. That he returned to England late in 1476 is attested by the 1477 Account Roll of John Esteney, sacrist of Westminster, where note is taken that a shop near the Abbey had been in the hands of a "Willo Caxton" for a year. Indeed, an indulgence appeared from Caxton's press as early as December 1476.

For roughly thirty-five years, then, Caxton lived in a Flemish-speaking area. That he began his Continental sojourn in Bruges is not absolutely certain, although it is plausible, since Bruges was from the Englishman's standpoint the import and export center of the Northern European textile trade in the latter half of the fifteenth century. The Mercer's Company of the Merchant Adventurers in Bruges was probably Caxton's first employer and his name appears in the *Registre des sentences civile de Bruges* in 1450 as one standing surety for a sum of £100 sterling. After nine years in Bruges, Caxton must have risen in the world, for only a reasonably wealthy man could have stood surety for such an amount. Twelve years later in 1462 he was important enough to act as the English deputy in Middleburg at the settlement of a cargo dispute. From 1463 to 1465 he was acting head of the Company; in 1465 he was appointed Governor of the English Nation at Bruges, having among other duties jurisdictional power over

32

resident English nationals. He continued in this position until 1470 or 1471. Whatever else Caxton may have been in these thirty-odd years, he was a successful businessman.

During the years 1471 to 1476, his last on the Continent, Caxton seems to have relinquished his duties as Governor, to have married, and to have assumed certain functions connected with the English diplomatic service. It is during these years that four people played an important role in his life and in consequence in the development of English printing and English literature. They arc the Duke and Duchess of Burgundy, Louis de Bruges, and Colard Mansion. All four have in common a background of French culture, although Margaret, Duchess of Burgundy, was the sister of Edward IV of England. Caxton probably met her in or around 1471 at the time of her marriage; he may have met Charles, Duke of Burgundy, four years earlier when he was attached to an English Royal Commission at the Burgundian Court. Both husband and wife were patrons of letters, French letters. Louis de Bruges, Seigneur de la Gruthuyse, possessed one of the finest libraries of the time and presumably Caxton was granted use of it. Henry Plomer in his *William Caxton* lists a number of works that undoubtedly would have been in the library of the Hotcl Gruthuyse and that Caxton would have seen. All the works Plomer cites are French. Colard Mansion, dean of the *Confrerie des libraires de Bruges*, was a French calligrapher and printer, and his association with Caxton is inferred from the fact that the two men were resident in Bruges at roughly the time when Caxton began his printing activities. At one time it was thought that Caxton learned printing from Mansion, a supposition now pretty well exploded by evidence that Caxton resided and indeed may have printed in Cologne in 1471. In fact, a recent study by T. A. Sheppard strongly urges that Mansion was the pupil and Caxton the master. At any event, historical as well as typographic inference still supports close association between the English mercer and the French scribe.

In the light of these associations, it is amazing that Caxton should have drawn a literary work from the submerged Flemish culture of Bruges, since especially during his last five years on the continent his literary and cultural contacts must have been predominantly French; and it is no little credit both to Caxton and the work itself that the only certain non-Romance work he translated is *Reynard the Fox*.

Contact with the first printer of the Reynard prose version, Gerard Leeu, cannot be supported as possible motivation for Caxton's choice. The life dates of Leeu and Caxton are roughly parallel, and the two men were fairly close geographically, at least up to 1476, but plausible evidence connecting them does not exist. To be sure, official documents show that in 1475 the town fathers of Gouda provided William Caxton, who was then in Gouda on official business, with a dinner. This fact does not lead to any conclusion. Leeu did not set up his own press in Gouda until 1477. When Leeu's *Reynaert* appeared in 1479, Caxton had been in England for three years. Neither a personal friendship nor a business association, in other words, can be adduced as the incentive behind Caxton's decision to print *Reynard the Fox* in 1481. Again we are left chiefly with the merit of the work and Caxton's critical sense as the deciding factors.

One feature of medieval English literature invariably catches the eye of the literary historian who is casting about to explain the sudden appearance of Reynard on the English literary scene in 1481. It is the Aesopic fable. Since there is no beast epic in English literature prior to 1481, the historian brings forth the animal fable as the nearest thing and implies that it prepared the public for Reynard. Such an observation is overly facile. An Aesopic fable is not a comic beast epic. The basic dramatis personae, animals, may be the same; nevertheless, the intent, the genre, and the tradition are different. The best view is that Caxton in 1481 introduced a genre, the comic beast epic, which the English people may have been in part prepared for by the Aesopic fable, especially in the form of the *exemplum* in sermons, but with which it was by no means intimately familiar.

R. M. Wilson in his *The Lost Literature of Medieval England* notes that Middle English is "surprisingly deficient in the beast story (p. 134)." There survive only three works predating Caxton's *Reynard* that are somewhat related to the comic beast epic. One is the beast fabliau called *The Vox and the Wolf*; it is anonymous, the manuscript is unique and its date placed somewhere in the last quarter of the thirteenth century. It tells the tale of the fox (he is given the name *Reneuard*, which indicates French provenience) falling into a well and then rescuing himself by enticing the wolf, whose name here is *Sigrim*, to climb into the upper bucket and thereby draw him to the surface. Another is a fifteenth century song called "The Fox and the Geese," which merely relates how a sly fox steals geese from a farm. The third is Chaucer's "Nonnes Prestes Tale." Here the folk element is very minor; the tale of the fox first duping a cock and then himself being duped is used chiefly as framework.

As we have seen in the preceding chapter, the emergence of a comic beast epic was a Continental affair, the result of several centuries of growth that reached its fruition in the Low Countries. One should not expect in England a tradition similar to the French or Flemish traditions; one may, however, be puzzled as to why England, usually so receptive especially to French literary influences, seems to have ignored almost completely one of the major international genres during the Middle Ages. To be sure, Odo of Cheriton and Marie de France among others got a fable tradition off to a good start in thirteenth century England, but the momentum seems not to have carried through. The earliest vernacular fables in England seem to be those of Lydgate in the early fifteenth century, and the first collection of fables in England in a form resembling the one familiar to us today is Caxton's *Esope* of 1484, which, incidentally, is derived from a Continental source. If an explanation is possible at all, it may be that the Continental bourgeoisie, for whom secular beast epics and beast fabliaux primarily existed, enjoyed greater consciousness of their own existence and individuality than did their English counterparts and were less likely to question the validity of a genre that was not sanctioned by the prevailing aristocratic taste.

Caxton's lexicographic significance is readily apparent to anyone who looks into the *Oxford English Dictionary* under words whose usage begins in the last quarter of the fifteenth century; here one may readily find words and new senses for existing words that Caxton introduced. In translating — and it must be remembered that he translated some twenty-odd works into English — Caxton had to introduce and innovate, for English was in his day not so fully possessed of a sound literary prose as was, for example, French.

Caxton's syntax in his translated pieces is invariably the syntax of his originals. Helmut Wiencke in his study *Die Sprache Caxtons* comes to this conclusion, as would anyone who carefully compared the syntax of Leeu's *Reynaert* with that of Caxton's translation of it. Caxton's concept of translation would lead nowhere but to the development of an idiom which could be called fifteenth century "translationese." In *The History of Jason*, Caxton says he is desirous of "following my autor as nygh as I can or may, not changyng ony thing otherwise than myne auctor hath made." Aristocratic contemporaries, perhaps conscious of the relative sophistication of French prose, were aware of Caxton's syntactic awkwardness and of his uncertainty with vocabulary. In the Prologue to *The Recuyell* Caxton says that the Duchess of Burgundy "fonde a defaute in myn English which she commanded me to amende." In the Prologue to *Eneydos*, one of the last works from Caxton's press and from his translator's pen, he makes the comment "Fayn wolde I satisfye every man" and regrets that "some gentylmen" accuse him of using "curyous terms which coude not be understande of comyn people." Other similar self-critical remarks could be adduced, all of which would indicate that Caxton was himself quite oblivious to the fact that he was with his "curyous terms" doing much to establish a vocabulary that in the following two centuries would appear in some of the finest prose in the whole of English literature.

36

Modern criticism of Caxton as a prose writer, apart from an evaluation of him as an innovator of language, is often unduly flattering. His prose, if read by modern aesthetic standards, is decidedly wooden. The charm lies in an idiom that seems no longer Chaucerian and much more archaic than Elizabethan, as well as in its rich and strange vocabulary and its difficult syntax. Charm it has, but it is one that must be sought after and worked up to. Some critics would lead us to believe that Caxton was a late fourteenth century Joseph Addison, and a student approaching Caxton's translations for the first time with only such critical orientation in mind is likely to be roundly disappointed.

K. N. Colvile's words are not very much different from those of various other critics. He writes in his "William Caxton: Man of Letters" (p. 170):

"Reynard the Fox" is political satire, but like most of the famous allegories, it is exceedingly good reading for its own intrinsic qualities. The character of Reynard is brought out with great subtlety and humor by the skill of Caxton's phrasing. He adopts with great success a deliberately familiar style, which strikes the reader of today as refreshingly modern and embodies many proverbial expressions. The verbs in such sentences as "I have carried on with dame Ersewynd his wife," and "he could not leave off looking after the poultry," may exemplify the first, and "that which cleaves by the bone may not out of the flesh," the second. Reynard, at the supposed point of death, is as pathetic as Falstaff, praising the greenwood (wherein in his lifetime he had invariably misconducted himself) and exclaiming unctuously, "Lord God, how sweet air is there!" The bettering of the state was . . . an aim Caxton had always in view, and one of his early Bruges printed books is of this type of political allegory — "The Game and Play of Chess."

First of all, *Reynard* is not "political satire"; it may be in part satirical, but it is chiefly a rather good-natured criticism of the human race in general. Nor is it allegory, if by that word is meant an extended and prolonged metaphor wherein a series of actions and a set of characters are consistently and primarily retained as equivalents of actions and characters existing on another level

37

of meaning. In *Reynard* narrative always takes precedence over this kind of allegory. That the "subtlety and humor" of *Reynard* is the result of "the skill of Caxton's phrasing" is debatable, to say the least. A critical reading even of the somewhat modernized edition that follows shows that Caxton was, at most, tactful on occasion in rewording a phrase he did not understand and also very much less than tactful in allowing passage to numerous vague expressions that even a fifteenth century reader might not have understood. "The deliberately familiar style" is more the result of Caxton's translating habits and the homely prose of his original, a Dutch chapbook, than the result of an innate feel for familiar style, a style in all probability he could not command in his prose translations, since his idea of translation went little beyond word-for-word substitution. The examples of "refreshingly modern" expressions which Colvile adduces would make one question the validity of his sampling. For every phrase as "refreshingly modern" as the two he quotes, there are literally dozens that are uncomfortably obscure and tortuous.

Some English writers and a few American tend to adopt a certain lofty ideological tone when treating Caxton. They are prone to equate Caxton's personality with the religious subject matter of most of his publications and with the patriotic verbiage found in some of his prologues and epilogues. A. T. P. Byles, for example, in his "William Caxton as a Man of Letters" (24f), assures us that "it was fortunate for England that her first printer was not a mercenary trader but a man of vision and high ideals." Another writer, of a genuinely significant reputation — Henry R. Plomer, in his *William Caxton 1424–1491* (p. 183f) —extols Caxton's piety and patriotism and little else: "That the printing press would sooner or later have been established in England is certain," he writes, "but it is well for the country that it was brought over by such a man as William Caxton, who put the fear of God and the good of his country before all other considerations, and who laid on a solid foundation the road which has led us to such high and noble results." Unfortunately, piety and patriotism do not necessarily predicate literary or human greatness, as such comments would strongly imply.

Equally unrewarding is the treatment that turns Caxton into an elderly moneyed dilettante with the implication that he did not really take his work in the Westminster printing shop seriously. Such a treatment is perhaps rarely expressed, but it is occasionally implicit in the comment of some bibliophiles. Nor does the dictum of Bernhard ten Brink at almost the opposite pole ring quite true, although it is immeasurably more valid. Caxton was, he writes in his *Geschichte der englischen Literatur* (p. 385; translation mine), "no great scholar and no profound thinker but a practical businessman intent chiefly on the practical and useful, [and] of restless prudent activity." Caxton admits in the Prologue to *Charles the Great* that he made his living from printing, and his printing of so many works of so many different kinds indicates a deadly serious desire to reach the book-buying public.

There is just one feature of Caxton as a man that these various evaluations fail to recognize: it is that he probably could tell good and enduring literature from the commonplace and merely timely. As has already been said, most of Caxton's seventy-seven publications (the number is arbitrary, but accurate enough here) were safe: patrons or an obvious public need assured him that his efforts would be financially rewarded. But when he published without such safeguards, he chose English poets — Chaucer, Gower, and Lydgate. Here he took a risk and must have had faith that intrinsic appeal would not make their production financially disastrous. Yet his ability to determine appeal, which at its best is the ability to perceive value, shows up well in his production of *Esope* and especially of *Reynard*. With each he not only seems to have taken a risk on a foreign book relatively unknown to his countrymen and for which his countrymen were not particularly prepared, but also seems to have succeeded in the venture. That he did so with *Reynard* is certain, for within two decades four editions of it had appeared, the second by Caxton of about 1489,

39

the third by Pynson assigned to 1494, and the fourth by de Worde probably before 1501. In this record there is certainly a distinction that one can claim for few other humanistic publications of early Tudor England.

THE HISTORY OF
REYNARD THE FOX

TRANSLATED AND PRINTED BY

WILLIAM CAXTON

JUNE

1481

The text of William Caxton's *The History of Reynard the Fox* appears in the following pages without any grammatical alterations or deletions, although modern orthography, punctuation, and paragraphing have been provided. A microfilm in the Houghton Library of Harvard University of a copy of the 1481 edition in the British Museum is the source, but readings in Thoms, Arber, and Stallybrass were consulted when problems arose concerning misprints and punctuation.

THIS IS THE TABLE OF
THE HISTORY OF REYNARD THE FOX

HERE BEGINS THE HISTORY OF

REYNARD THE FOX

IN this history be written the parables, good lering, and
diverse points to be marked, by which points men may learn
to come to the subtle knowledge of such things as daily be
used and had in the councils of lords and prelates, ghostly and
worldly, and also among merchants and other common people.
And this book is made for need and profit of all good folk,
as far as they in reading or hearing of it shall more understand
and feel the foresaid subtle deceits that daily be used in the
world, not to the intent that men should use them, but that
every man should eschew and keep him from the subtle false
shrews that they be not deceived. Then who that will have
the very understanding of this matter, he must oft and many
times read in this book and earnestly and diligently mark well
that he reads, for it is set subtly, like as you shall see in reading
of it, and not once to read it, for a man shall not with once
over reading find the right understanding nor comprise it well;
but oftimes to read it shall cause it well to be understood. And
for them that understand it, it shall be right joyous, pleasant,
and profitable.

1. *How the Lion, King of All Beasts, Sent Out His Mandments
That All Beasts Should Come to His Feast and Court*

It was about the time of Pentecost or Whitsuntide[1] that the
woods commonly be lusty and gladsome and the trees clad

lering: doctrine	*ghostly*: spiritual	*eschew*: avoid
shrew: rogue	*comprise*: comprehend	*mandment*: command-ment
lusty: merry		

45

with leaves and blossoms and the ground with herbs and flowers sweet smelling and also the fowls and birds sing melodiously in their harmony that the lion, the noble king of all beasts, would in the holy days of this feast hold an open court at Stade,[2] which he did to know[3] over all his land. And commanded by strait commissions and mandments that every beast should come thither in such wise that all the beasts, great and small, came to the court, save Reynard[4] the fox, for he knew himself faulty and guilty in many things against many beasts that thither should come that he dared not adventure to go thither when the king of all beasts had assembled all his court. There was none of them all but that he had complained sore on Reynard the fox.

11. *The First Complaint Made Isegrim[5] the Wolf on Reynard*

Isegrim the wolf with his lineage and friends came and stood tofore the king and said, "High and mighty prince, my lord the king, I beseech you that through your great might, right, and mercy that you will have pity on the great trespass and the unreasonable misdeeds that Reynard the fox has done to me and to my wife; that is to wit, he has come into my house against the will of my wife, and there he has bepissed my children whereas they lay in such wise as they thereof be waxen blind.

"Whereupon was a day set and was judged that Reynard should come and have excused him hereof and have sworn on the holy saints that he was not guilty thereof. And when the book with the saints was brought forth, tho had Reynard bethought him otherwise and went his way again into his hole

strait: strict   adventure: risk   tofore: before
whereas: where   waxen: grown   tho: then
him: himself

as he had nought set thereby.[6] And, dear king, this know well many of the beasts that now be come hither to your court. And yet hath he trespassed to me in many other things. He is

Isegrim the wolf with his lineage and friends came and stood tofore
the king

not living that could tell all that I now leave untold. But the shame and villainy that he has done to my wife, that shall I never hide nor suffer it unavenged, but that he shall make to me large amends."

47

III. *The Complaint of Curtois* [7] *the Hound*

When these words were spoken, so stood there a little hound and was named Curtois and complained to the king how that in the cold winter in the hard frost, he had been sore for-wintered [8] in such wise as he had kept no more meat than a pudding, which pudding Reynard the fox had taken away from him.

Tho Spoke Tibert [9] the Cat

With this so came Tibert the cat with an irous mood and sprang in among them and said, "My lord the king, I hear here that Reynard is sore complained on and here is none but that he had enough to do to clear himself. That Curtois here complains of, that is passed many years ago. How be it that I complain not? That pudding was mine, for I had won it by night in the mill. The miller lay and slept. If Curtois had any part hereon, that came by me too."

Then spoke panther, "Think you, Tibert, that it were good that Reynard should not be complained on? He is a very murderer, a rover, and a thief. He loves no man so well, not our lord the king here, that he well would that he should lose good and worship so that he might win as much as a leg of a fat hen. I shall tell you what I saw him do yesterday to Cuwart [10] the hare that here stands in the king's peace and safeguard. He promised to Cuwart and said he would teach him his credo and make him a good chaplain. He made him go sit between his legs and sang and cried loud, 'Credo! Credo!' My way lay thereby there that I heard this sung. Tho went I near and found Master Reynard that had left that he first read and sung and began to play the old play, for he had caught Cuwart by the throat; and had I not that time come, he should

---

pudding: sausage   *irous*: angry   *rover*: robber

have taken his life from him, like as you here may see on Cuwart the hare the fresh wound yet. Forsooth, my lord the king, if you suffer this unpunished and let him go quit that has thus broken your peace and will do no right after the sentence and judgment of your men, your children many years hereafter shall be misprized and blamed therefore."

"Sikerly, panther," said Isegrim, "you say the truth! It were good that right and justice were done for them that would fain live in peace."

IV. *How Grimbert* [11] *the Dasse,* [12] *the Fox's Sister's Son, Spoke for Reynard and Answered Tofore the King*

Tho spoke Grimbert the dasse and was Reynard's sisterson [13] with an angry mood, "Sir Isegrim, that is evil said! It is a common proverb 'An enemy's mouth says seld well.' What lie you and wite you my eme Reynard? I would that you would adventure that who of you twain had most trespassed to other should hang by the neck as a thief on a tree. But and if he were as well in this court and as well with the king as you be, it should not be thought in him that it were enough that you should come and ask him forgiveness. [14] You have bitten and nipped my uncle with your fell and sharp teeth many more times than I can tell. Yet will I tell some points that I well know. Know not you how you misdealed on the plaice which he threw down from the car when you followed after from afar. And you ate the good plaice alone and gave him no more than the grate or bones which you might not eat yourself. In like wise did you to him also of the fat flitch of bacon which savored so well that you alone ate in your belly; and when my

quit: free	*misprized*: scorned	*sikerly*: surely
dasse: badger	*seld*: seldom	*wite*: blame
eme: uncle	*fell*: cruel	*car*: cart
grate: fishbone	*flitch*: side	

49

eme asked his part, tho answered you him again in scorn, 'Reynard, fair youngling, I shall gladly give you your part.' But my eme got nor had nought nor was not the better, notwithstanding he had won the flitch of bacon with great dread, for the man came and threw him in a sack that he scarcely came out with his life. Such manner things has Reynard many times suffered through Isegrim.

"Oh you lords, think you that this is good? Yet is there more! He complains how that Reynard, my eme, has much trespassed to him because of his wife. My eme has lain by her, but that is well seven year tofore ere he wedded her. And if Reynard for love and courtesy did with her his will, what was that? She was soon healed thereof. Hereof by rights should be no complaint were Isegrim wise. He should have left that. He does to himself no worship thus to slander his wife. She complains not. Now makes Cuwart the hare a complaint also. That thinks me a vysevase.[15] If he read nor learned aright his lesson, should not Reynard his master beat him therefor? If the scholars were not beaten nor smitten and reprised of their truantry, they should never learn.

"Now complains Curtois that he with pain had gotten a pudding in the winter at such time as the cost is evil to find. Thereof him had be better to have held his peace, for he had stolen it. Male quesisti et male perdidisti. It is right that it be evil lost that is evil won. Who shall blame Reynard if he has taken from a thief stolen goods? It is reason. Who that understands the law and can discern the right, and that he be of high birth as my eme Reynard is, which knows well how he shall receive stolen goods, yet all had he Curtois hanged when he found him with the mainour.[16] He had not much misdone nor

---

dread: peril   *worship*: credit   *vysevase*: folly
reprised: reproached   *cost*: food   *mainour*: plunder

trespassed save against the crown that he had done justice without leave. Wherefore for the honor of the king he did it not, all had he but little thanks. What scathed it him that he is thus complained on? My eme is a gentle and true man. He may suffer no falsehood. He does nothing but by his priest's counsel; and I say you, sith that my lord the king has done proclaimed his peace, he never thought to hurt any man. For he eats no more than once a day. He lives as a recluse. He chastises his body and wears a shirt of hair. It is more than a year that he has eaten no flesh, as I yesterday heard say of them that came from him. He has left and given over his castle Maleperduys [17] and has built a close. Therein dwells he and hunts no more nor desires no winning; but he lives by alms and takes nothing but such as men give him for charity and does great penance for his sins; and he is waxed much pale and lean of praying and waking, for he would be fain with God."

Thus as Grimbert, his eme,[18] stood and preached these words, so saw they come down the hill to them Chanticleer [19] the cock, and brought on a bier a dead hen, of whom Reynard had bitten the head off and that must be showed to the king for to have knowledge thereof.

v. How the Cock Complained on Reynard

Chanticleer came forth and smote piteously his hands and his feathers; and on each side of the bier went two sorrowful hens. That one was called Cantart [20] and that other good hen Crayant.[21] They were two the fairest hens that were between Holland and Ardennes. These hens bore each of them a burning taper, which was long and straight. These two hens were Coppen's [22] sisters and they cried so piteously "Alas and well

scathed: hurt   *sith*: since   *close*: hermitage
winning: gain

51

away" for the death of their dear sister Coppen. Two young hens bore the bier, which cackled so heavily and wept so loud for the death of Coppen, their mother, that it was far heard. Thus came they together tofore the king.

And Chanticleer tho said, "Merciful lord, my lord the king, please it you to hear our complaint and abhor the great scathe that Reynard has done to me and my children that here stand. It was so that in the beginning of April when the weather is fair and that I am hardy and proud because of the great lineage that I am come of and also had, for I had eight fair sons and seven fair daughters which my wife had hatched. And they were all strong and fat and went in a yard which was walled round about, in which was a shed wherein were six great dogs which had totorn and plucked many a beast's skin in such wise as my children were not afraid. On whom Reynard the thief had great envy because they were so sure that he could none get of them. How well oftimes has this fell thief gone round about this wall and has laid for us in such wise that the dogs have been set on him and have hunted him away. And once they leaped on him upon the bank and that cost him somewhat for his theft. I saw that his skin smoked;[23] nevertheless, he went his way, God amend it!

"Thus we were quit of Reynard a long while. At last came he in likeness of a hermit and brought to me a letter for to read, sealed with the king's seal, in which stood written that the king had made peace over all his realm and that all manner beasts and fowls should do no harm nor scathe to any other. Yet said he to me more, that he was a cloisterer or a closed recluse become and that he would receive great penance for his sins. He showed me his slavin and pilch [24] and a hair shirt thereunder.

totorn: shredded   *slavin*: mantle   *pilch*: cloak

"And then said he, 'Sir Chanticleer, after this time be no more afraid of me nor take no heed, for I now will eat no more flesh. I am forthon [25] so old that I would fain remember my soul. I will now go forth, for I have yet to say my sext, none, [26] and my evensong. To God I betake you!'

"Tho went Reynard thence, saying his credo, and laid him under a hawthorn. Then was I glad and merry and also took no heed and went to my children and clucked them together and went without the wall for to walk, whereof was much harm come to us. For Reynard lay under a bush and came creeping between us and the gate so that he caught one of my children and laid him in his mail, whereof we have had great harm. For sith he has tasted of him, there might never hunter nor hound save nor keep him from us. He has waited by night and day in such wise that he has stolen so many of my children that of fifteen I have but four.

"In such wise has this thief forslongen [27] them. And yet yesterday was Coppen my daughter that here lies upon the bier with the hounds rescued. This complain I to you, gracious king; have pity on my great and unresasonable damage and loss of my fair children."

vi. *How the King Spoke Touching This Complaint*

Then spoke the king, "Sir Dasse, hear you this well of the recluse, your eme? He has fasted and prayed that if I live a year he shall aby it. Now hark, Chanticleer, your plaint is enough. Your daughter that lies here dead, we will give to her the death's rite. We may keep her no longer. We will betake her to God. We will sing her vigils and bring her worshipfully on earth and then we will speak with these lords and take

forthon: henceforth   *mail*: bag   *forslongen*: devoured
aby: atone for

counsel how we may do right and justice of this great murder and bring this false thief to the law."

Tho began they Placebo Domino,[28] with the verses that to longen. When this vigil was done and the commendation, she was laid in the pit and thereupon was laid a marble stone, polished as clear as any glass, and thereon was hewn in great letters in this wise, "Coppen, Chanticleer's Daughter, Whom Reynard the Fox Has Bitten, Lies Hereunder Buried. Complain You for Her! She Is Shamefully Come to Her Death."

After this the king sent for his lords and wisest of his council for to take advice how this great murder and trespass should be punished on Reynard the fox. There was concluded and appointed for the best that Reynard should be sent for and that he left not for any cause, but he come into the king's court for to hear what should be said to him and that Bruin [29] the bear should do the message.

The king thought that all this was good and said to Bruin the bear, "Sir Bruin, I will that you do this message, but see well to for yourself, for Reynard is a shrew and fell and knows so many wiles that he shall lie and flatter and shall think how he may beguile, deceive, and bring you to some mockery."

Tho said Bruin, "What, good lord, let it alone! Deceives me the fox, so have I ill learned my *casus*.[30] I trow he shall come too late to mock me!"

Thus departed Bruin merrily from them, but it is to dread that he came not so merrily again.

VII. *How Bruin the Bear Was Sped of Reynard the Fox*

Now is Bruin gone on his way for the fox with a stout mood, which supposed well that the fox should not have be-

to: thereto   *longen*: belong   *casus*: ABC's
sped: handled

guiled him. As he came in a dark wood in a forest whereas Reynard had a by-path when he was hunted, there beside was a high mountain and land and there must Bruin in the middle go over for to go to Maleperduys. For Reynard had many a dwelling place, but the castle of Maleperduys was the best and fastest burg that he had. There lay he in when he had need and was in any dread or fear.

Now when Bruin was come to Maleperduys, he found the gate fast shut. Tho went he tofore the gate and sat upon his tail and called, "Reynard, be you at home? I am Browning.[31] The king has sent me for you that you should come to court for to plead your case. He has sworn there by his God, come you not or bring I you not with me for to abide such right and sentence as shall be there given, it shall cost you your life. He will hang you or set you on the rat.[32] Reynard, do by my counsel and come to court."

Reynard lay within the gate as he oft was wont to do for the warmth of the sun. When Reynard heard Bruin, tho went he inward into his hole, for Maleperduys was full of holes, here one hole and there another and yonder another, narrow, crooked, and long, with many ways to go out, which he opened and shut after that he had need. When he had any prey brought home or that he wist that any sought him for his misdeeds and trespasses, then he ran and hid him from his enemies into his secret chambers that they could not find him, by which he deceived many a beast that sought him. And tho thought Reynard in himself how he might best bring the bear in charge and need and that he abide in worship.

In this thought, Reynard came out and said, "Bruin, eme, you be welcome. I heard you well tofore, but I was in my

burg: fortress	*rat*: wheel	*wist*: knew
charge: straits	*worship*: honor	

evensong. Therefore have I longer tarried a little. Dear eme, he has done to you no good service and I can him no thank that has sent you over this long hill, for I see that you be also weary that the sweat runs down by your cheeks. It was no need. I had nevertheless come to court tomorrow, but I sorrow now the less, for your wise counsel shall well help me in the court. And could the king find no less messenger but you for to send hither, that is great wonder, for next the king you be the most gentle and richest of levies and of land. I would well that we were now at the court, but I fear me that I shall not con well go thither, for I have eaten so much new meat that methinks that my belly will break or cleave asunder and because the meat was new, I ate the more."

Tho spoke the bear, "Lief nephew, what meat have you eaten that makes you so full?"

"Dear eme, that I eat? What might it help you that if I told you? I eat but simple meat. A poor man is no lord; that may you know, eme, by me. We poor folk must eat oftimes such as we gladly would not eat if we had better. They were great honeycombs which I must needs eat for hunger. They have made my belly so great that I can nowhere endure."

Bruin tho spoke anon, "Alas, Reynard, what say you? Set you so little by honey? Me ought to prize and love it above all meat! Lief Reynard, help me that I might get a deal of this honey and as long as I live, I shall be to you a true friend and abide by you as far as you help me that I may have a part of this honey."

viii. *How Bruin Ate the Honey*

"Bruin, eme, I had supposed that you had japed therewith!"

| *also*: so | *con*: be able to | *meat*: food |
| *lief*: dear | *jape*: joke | |

"So help me God, Reynard! Nay, I should not gladly jape with you."

Then spoke the red [33] Reynard, "Is it then earnest that you love so well the honey? I shall do let you have so much that ten of you should not eat it at one meal, might I get therewith your friendship."

"Not we ten, Reynard, never!" said the bear. "How should that be? Had I all the honey that is between this and Portugal, I should eat it alone."

Reynard said, "What say you, eme, hereby dwells a husbandman named Lantfert,[34] which has so much honey that you should not eat it in seven years, which you shall have in your hold if you will be to me friendly and helping against my enemies in the king's court."

Then promised Bruin the bear to him that if he might have his belly full he would truly be to him tofore all other a faithful friend. Hereof laughed Reynard the shrew and said, "If you would have seven hamber [35] barrels full, I shall well get them and help you to have them." These words pleased the bear so well and made him so much to laugh that he could not well stand. Tho thought Reynard, "This is good luck. I shall lead him thither that he shall laugh by measure."

Reynard said then, "This matter may not be long tarried. I must pain myself for you. You shall well understand the very yonst [36] and good will that I bear to youward. I know none in all my lineage that I now would labor for thus sore."

That thanked him the bear and thought he tarried long.

"Now, eme, let us go a good pace and follow you me. I shall make you to have as much honey as you may bear." The fox meant of good strokes, but the caitiff marked not what the fox meant and they went so long together that they came unto Lantfert's yard. Tho was Sir Bruin merry.

yonst: favor

57

Now hark of Lantfert. It is true that men say, so was Lantfert a strong carpenter of great timber and had brought that other day tofore into his yard a great oak which he had begun to cleave. And as men be wont, he had smitten two betels therein one after that other, in such wise the oak was wide open, whereof Reynard was glad, for he had found it right as he wished.

And said to the bear all laughing, "See now well sharply to! In this tree is so much honey that it is without measure. Assay if you can come therein and eat but little, for though the honeycombs be sweet and good, yet beware that you eat not too many, but take of them by measure that you catch no harm in your body. For, sweet eme, I should be blamed if they did you any harm."

"What, Reynard cousin, sorrow you not for me! Ween you that I were a fool? Measure is good in all meat."

Reynard said, "You say truth. Wherefore should I sorrow? Go to the end and creep therein."

Bruin the bear hastened sore toward the honey and tread in with his two foremost feet and put his head over his ears into the cleft. And Reynard sprang lightly and broke out the betel of the tree.

Tho helped the bear neither flattery nor chiding. He was fast shut in the tree. Thus had the nephew with deceit brought his eme in prison in the tree in such wise as he could not get out with might nor with craft, head nor foot. What profited Bruin the bear that he strong and hardy is! That may not help him. He saw well that he beguiled was. He began to howl and to bray and crutched [37] with the hinder feet and made such a noise and rumor that Lantfert came out hastily and knew

betels: wedges   *ween*: think   *rumor*: uproar

nothing what this might be and brought in his hand a sharp hook.

Bruin the bear lay in the cleft of the tree in great fear and dread and held fast his head and nipped both his forefeet. He wrung, he wrestled, and cried and all was for nought. He wist not how he might get out.

Reynard the fox saw from far how that Lantfert the carpenter came and tho spoke Reynard to the bear, "Is that good honey? How is it now? Eat not too much, it should do you harm; you should not then well con go to the court. When Lantfert comes, if you have well eaten, he shall give you better to drink and then it shall not stick in your throat."

After these words, tho turned him Reynard toward his castle; and Lantfert came and found the bear fast taken in the tree. Then ran he fast to his neighbors and said, "Come all into my yard. There is a bear taken!" The word anon sprang over all in the thorpe. There nor bleef neither man nor wife, but all ran thither as fast as they could, everyone with his weapon, some with a staff, some with a rake, some with a broom, some with a stake of a hedge,[38] and some with a flail; and the priest of the church had the staff of the cross and the clerk brought a vane. The priest's wife [39] Julock [40] came with her distaff; she sat tho and spun.[41] There came old women that for age had not one tooth in their head.

Now was Bruin the bear nigh much sorrow that he alone must stand against them all. When he heard all this great noise and cry, he wrestled and plucked so hard and so sore that he got out his head, but he left behind all the skin and both his ears in such wise that never man saw fouler nor loathlier beast, for the blood ran over his eyes and or he could get out

thorpe: town   *bleef*: tarried   *vane*: banner
or: before

his feet, he must let there his claws or nails and his rough hand. This market [42] came to him evil, for he supposed never to have gone, his feet were so sore; and he might not see for the blood which ran so over his eyes.

Lantfert came to him with the priest and forth with all the parish and began to smite and strike sore upon his head and visage. He received there many a sore stroke. Every man beware hereby who has harm and scathe; every man will be thereat and put more to. That was well seen on the bear, for they were all fierce and wroth on the bear, great and small. Yes, Hughelin [43] with the crooked leg and Ludolf [44] with the broad long nose, they were both wroth. That one had a leaden maul and the other a great leaden wapper,[45] therewith they wappered and all forslingered [46] him. Sir Bertolt [47] with the long fingers, Lantfert and Ottram [48] the long, these did to the bear more harm than all the other. That one had a sharp hook and that other a crooked staff well-leaded on the end for to play at the ball. Baetkin [49] and Ave [50] Abelquak,[51] my Dame Bave,[52] and the priest with his staff, and Dame Julock his wife, these wrought to the bear so much harm that they would fain have brought him from his life to death. They smote and stuck him all that they could.

Bruin the bear sat and sighed and groaned and must take such as was given to him. But Lantfert was the worthiest of birth of them all and made most noise for Dame Pogge of Chafport [53] was his mother and his father Macob the stopple maker,[54] a much strong man. Thereas he was alone, Bruin received of them many a cast of stones. Tofore them all sprang forth Lantfert's brother with a staff and smote the bear on the head that he nor heard nor saw and therewith the bear sprang up between the bush and the river among a heap of wives that he

wapper: truncheon   *wappered*: slugged   *forslingered*: beat

threw a deal of them in the river, which was wide and deep.

There was the parson's wife one of them; wherefore he was full of sorrow when he saw his wife lie in the water. Him lusted no longer to smite the bear, but called, "Dame Julock in the water! Now every man see to! All they that may help her, be they men or women, I give to them all pardon of their penance and release all their sins." All they then left Bruin the bear lie and did that the priest bade.

When Bruin the bear saw that they ran all from him and ran to save the women, tho sprang he into the water and swam all that he could. Then made the priest a great shout and noise and ran after the bear with great anger and said, "Come and turn again you false thief!"

The bear swam after the best of the stream [55] and let them call and cry for he was glad that he was so escaped from them. He cursed and banned the honey tree and the fox also that had so betrayed him, that he had crept therein so deep, that he lost both his hood and his ears, and so forth. He drove in the stream well a two or three miles. Tho waxed he so weary that he went to land for to sit and rest him for he was heavy. He groaned and sighed, and the blood lept over his eyes. He drew his breath like as one should have died.

Now hark how the fox did. Ere he came from Lantfert's house, he had stolen a fat hen and had laid her in his mail and ran hastily away by a bypath where he weened that no man should have come. He ran toward the river that he sweat. He was so glad that he wist not what to do for joy, for he hoped that the bear had been dead.

He said, "I have now well sped, for he that should most have hindered me in the court is now dead and none shall wite me thereof. May I not then by right be well glad?" With these

banned: cursed   *drove*: drifted

words the fox looked to the riverward and espied where Bruin the bear lay and rested him. Tho was the fox sorrier and heavier than tofore was merry and was as angry and said in chiding to Lantfert, "Alas, Lantfert, lewd fool! God give him a shame's death that has lost such good venison, which is good and fat, and has let him go which was taken to his hand. Many a man would gladly have eaten of him. He has lost a rich and fat bear."

Thus all chiding he came to the river, where he found the bear sore wounded, bebled, and right sick, which he might thank none better thereof than Reynard, which spoke to the bear in scorn, "Chiere preistre, dieu vous garde!" [56]

"Will you see the red thief," said the bear to himself, "the ribald and the fell dier, [57] here I see him come!"

Then said the fox, "Have you ought forgotten at Lantfert's? Have you also paid him for the honeycombs that you stole from him? If you have not, it were a great shame and not honest. I will rather be the messenger myself for to go and pay him. Was the honey not good? I know yet more of the same price. Dear eme, tell me ere I go hence into what order will you go that wear this new hood? Were you a monk or an abbot, he that shaved your crown has nipped off your ears. You have lost your top and done off your gloves. I trow verily that you will go sing compline." [58]

All this heard Bruin the bear and waxed all angry and sorry, for he might not avenge himself. He let the fox say his will and with great pain suffered it and started again in the river and swam down with the stream to the other side. Now must he sorrow how that he should come to the court, for he had lost his ears and the skin with the claws of his forefeet. For

bebled: bloody   *ribald*: knave   *dier*: animal

though a man should have slain him, he could not go and yet he must needs forth, but he wist not how.

Now hear how he did. He sat upon his hams and began to rutsel over his tail and when he was so weary, he wentled and tumbled nigh half a mile. This did he with great pain so long till at last he came to the court. And when he was seen so coming from far, some doubted what it might be that came so wentling.

The king at last knew him and was not well paid and said, "This is Bruin the bear, my friend! Lord God, who has wounded him thus? He is passing red on the head. Methinks he is hurt unto the death. Where may he have been?"

Therewith is the bear come tofore the king and said:

IX. *The Complaint of the Bear Upon the Fox*

"I complain to you, merciful lord, sir king, so as you may see how that I am handled, praying you to avenge it upon Reynard, the fell beast, for I have gotten this in your service. I have lost both my foremost feet, my cheeks, and my ears by his false deceit and treason."

The king said, "How dares this false thief Reynard do this! I say to you Bruin and swear by my crown I shall so avenge you on him that you shall con me thank."

He sent for all the wise beasts and desired counsel how that he might avenge this overgreat wrong that the fox had done. Then the council concluded, old and young, that he should be sent for and dayed earnestly again for to abide such judgment as should there be given on him of all his trespasses; and they thought that the cat Tibert might best do this message if he would, for he is right wise. The king thought this counsel good.

rutsel: slide   *wentled*: twisted   *paid*: pleased

63

x. *How the King Sent Another Time Tibert the Cat for the Fox and How Tibert Sped with Reynard the Fox*

Then the king said, "Sir Tibert, you shall now go to Reynard and say to him this second time that he come to court unto the plea for to answer, for though he be fell to other beasts he trusts you well and shall do by your counsel. And tell if he come not, he shall have the third warning and be dayed and if he then come not, we shall proceed by right against him and all his lineage without mercy."

Tibert spoke, "My lord the king, they that this counselled you were not my friends. What shall I do there? He will not for me neither come nor abide. I beseech you, dear king, send some other to him. I am little and feeble. Bruin the bear, which was so great and strong, could not bring him. How should I then take it on hand?"

"Nay," said the king, "Sir Tibert, you be wise and well learned. Though you be not great, there lies not on;[59] many do more with craft and cunning than with might and strength."

Then said the cat, "Sith it must needs be done, I must then take it upon me. God give grace that I may well achieve it, for my heart is heavy and evil willed thereto." Tibert made him soon ready toward Maleperduys, and he saw from far come flying one of Saint Martin's birds.[60] Tho cried he loud and said, "All hail, gentle bird, turn your wings hitherward and fly on my right side." The bird flew forth upon a tree which stood on the left side of the cat. Tho was Tibert woe, for he thought it was a shrewd token and a sign of harm. For if the bird had flown on his right side, he had been merry and glad; but now he sorrowed that his journey should turn to unhap. Nevertheless, he did as many do and gave to himself better hope than his heart said. He went and ran to Maleper-

dayed: summoned   *shrewd*: evil   *unhap*: misfortune duys and there he found the fox alone standing tofore his house.

Tibert said, "The rich God give you good even, good Reynard! The king has menaced you for to take your life from you, if you come not now with me to the court."

The fox tho spoke and said, "Tibert, my dear cousin, you be right welcome! I would well truly that you had much good luck." What hurt the fox to speak fair? Though he said well, his heart thought it not and that shall be seen ere they depart.

The fox tho said, "Will we this night be together, I will make you good cheer and tomorrow early in the dawning, we will together go to the court. Good nephew, let us so do. I have none of my kin that I trust so much to as to you. Here was Bruin the bear, the traitor. He looked so shrewdly on me and methought he was so strong that I would not for a thousand marks have gone with him. But, cousin, I will tomorrow early go with you."

Tibert said, "It is best that we now go for the moon shines all so light as it were day. I never saw fairer weather."

"Nay, dear cousin, such might meet us by daytime that would make us good cheer and by night peradventure might do us harm. It is suspicious to walk by night. Therefore, abide this night here by me."

Tibert said, "What should we eat if we abode here?"

Reynard said, "Here is but little to eat. You may well have a honeycomb, good and sweet. What say you, Tibert, will you any thereof?"

Tibert answered, "I set nought thereby. Have you nothing else? If you gave me a good fat mouse, I should be better pleased."

"A fat mouse," said Reynard, "dear cousin, what say you? Hereby dwells a priest and has a barn by his house; therein be so many mice that a man should not lead them away upon a wain. I have heard the priest many times complain that they did him much harm."

"Oh, dear Reyner,[61] lead me thither for all that I may do for you!"

"Yes, Tibert, say you me truth? Love you well mice?"

"If I love them well!" said the cat. "I love mice better than anything that men give me. Know you not that mice savor better than venison, yes, than flawnes or pasties? Will you well do, so lead me thither where the mice be and then shall you win my love, yes, all had you slain my father, mother, and all my kin!"

Reynard said, "You mock and jape therewith!"

The cat said, "So help me God, I do not!"

"Tibert," said the fox, "wist I that verily I would yet this night make that you should be full of mice."

"Reynard," quod he, "full? That were many!"

"Tibert, you jape."

"Reynard," quod he, "in truth I do not. If I had a fat mouse, I would not give it for a golden noble."

"Let us go then, Tibert," quod the fox. "I will bring you to the place ere I go from you."

"Reyner," quod the fox,[62] "upon your safe-conduct I would well go with you to Montpelier." [63]

"Let us then go," said the fox, "we tarry all too long."

Thus went they forth without letting to the place whereas they would be, to the priest's barn, which was fast walled about with a mud wall and the night tofore the fox had broken in and had stolen from the priest a good fat hen and the priest all angry had set a grin tofore the hole to avenge him, for he

wain: wagon	*flawnes*: flat cakes	*noble*: coin
letting: stopping	*grin*: snare	

would fain have taken the fox. This knew well the fell thief, the fox, and said, "Sir Tibert, cousin, creep into this hole and you shall not long tarry but that you shall catch mice by great heaps. Hark, how they peep! When you be full, come again. I will tarry here after you before this hole. We will tomorrow go together to the court. Tibert, why tarry you thus long? Come off and so may we return soon to my wife, which waits after us and shall make us good cheer."

Tibert said, "Reynard, cousin, is it then your counsel that I go into this hole? These priests be so wily and shrewish. I dread to take harm."

"Oho, Tibert," said the fox, "I saw you never so sore afraid. What ails you?"

The cat was ashamed and sprang into the hole. And anon he was caught in the grin by the neck ere he wist. Thus deceived Reynard his guest and cousin.

As Tibert was ware of the grin, he was afraid and sprang forth. The grin went to. Then began he to wrawen, for he was almost ystrangled.[64] He called, he cried, and made a shrewd noise.

Reynard stood tofore the hole and heard all and was well apaid and said, "Tibert, love you well mice? Be they fat and good? Knew the priest hereof or Martinet,[65] they be so gentle that they would bring you sauce. Tibert, you sing and eat! Is that the guise of the court? Lord God, if Isegrim were there by you in such rest as you now be, then should I be glad, for oft he has done me scathe and harm."

Tibert could not go away, but he meowed and yelped so loud that Martinet sprang up and cried loud, "God be thanked, my grin has taken the thief that has stolen our hen! Arise up, we will reward him!"

come off: hurry   *wrawen*: meow   *apaid*: pleased

With these words arose the priest in an evil time [66] and waked all them that were in the house and cried with a loud voice, "The fox is taken!"

They lept and ran, all that there was. The priest himself ran all mothernaked. Martinet was the first that came to Tibert. The priest took to Locken,[67] his wife, an offering candle and bade her light it at the fire and he smote Tibert with a great staff. There received Tibert many a great stroke over all his body. Martinet was so angry that he smote the cat an eye out. The naked priest lifted up and should have given a great stroke to Tibert, but Tibert, that saw that he must die, sprang between the priest's legs with his claws and with his teeth that he wrought out his right cullion or ballock stone. That leap became ill to the priest.

This thing fell down upon the floor. When Dame Julock knew that, she swore by her father's soul that she would it had cost her all the offering of a whole year that the priest had not had that harm, hurt, and shame and that it had not happened and said, "In the devil's name was the grin there set! See Martinet, lief son, this is of thy father's harness. This is a great shame and to me a great hurt, for though he be healed thereof yet he is but a lost man to me and also shall never con do that sweet play and game."

The fox stood without tofore the hole and heard all these words and laughed so sore that he uneath could stand. He spoke thus all softly, "Dame Julock, be all still and your great sorrow sink. All has the priest lost one of his stones, it shall not hinder him. He shall do with you well enough. There is in this world many a chapel in which is rung but one bell." Thus scorned and mocked the fox the priest's wife, Dame Julock, that was full of sorrow.

cullion: testicle   *ballock stone*: testicle   *harness*: genital
uneath: hardly

The priest fell down aswoon. They took him up and brought him again to bed. Tho went the fox again into his burrowward and left Tibert the cat in great dread and jeopardy, for the fox wist none other but that the cat was nigh dead. But when Tibert the cat saw them all busy about the priest, tho began he to bite and gnaw the grin in the middle asunder and sprang out of the hole and went rolling and wentling toward the king's court. Or he came thither, it was fair day and the sun began to rise. And he came to the court as a poor wight. He had caught harm at the priest's house by the help and counsel of the fox. His body was all tobeaten and blind on the one eye. When the king wist this that Tibert was thus arrayed, he was sore angry and menaced Reynard the thief sore and anon gathered his council to wit that they would advise him how he might bring the fox to the law and how he should be fetched.

Tho spoke Sir Grimbert, which was the fox's sister's son, and said, "You lords, though my eme were twice so bad and shrewish, yet is there remedy enough. Let him be done to as to a free man. When he shall be judged, he must be warned the third time.[68] For all and if he comes not then he is then guilty in all the trespasses that be laid against him and his or complained on."

"Grimbert, who would you that should go and day him to come? Who will adventure for him his ears, his eye, or his life, which is so fell a beast? I trow there is none here so much a fool."

Grimbert spoke, "So help me God, I am so much a fool that I will do this message myself to Reynard, if you will command me."

wight: fellow   *tobeaten*: beaten to   *wit*: know
                                                   pieces

xi. *How Grimbert the Dasse Brought the Fox to the Law Tofore the King*

"Now go forth, Grimbert, and see well tofore you. Reynard is so fell and false and so subtle that you need well to look about you and to beware of him."

Grimbert said that he should see well to. Thus went Grimbert to Maleperduys-ward and when he came thither, he found Reynard the fox at home and Dame Ermelin [69] lay by her whelps in a dark corner.

Tho spoke Grimbert and saluted his eme and his aunt and said to Reynard, "Eme, beware that your absence hurt you not in such matters as be laid and complained on you. But if you think it good, it is high time that you come with me to the court. The withholding you from it can do you no good. There is much thing complained over you and this is the third warning and I tell you for truth if you abide tomorrow all day, there may no mercy help you. You shall see that within three days that your house shall be besieged all about and there shall be made tofore it gallows and rack. I say you truly, you shall not then escape neither with wife nor with child. The king shall take all your lives from you. Therefore it is best that you go with me to the court. Your subtle wise counsel shall peradventure avail you. There be greater adventures fallen ere this,[70] for it may hap you shall go quit of all the complaints that be complained on you and all your enemies shall abide in the shame. You have oftimes done more and greater things than this."

Reynard the fox answered, "You say sooth. I trow it is best that I go with you, for there lacks my counsel. Preadventure the king shall be merciful to me if I may come to speak with him and see him under his eyes. Though I had done much more harm, the court may not stand without me. That shall the king well understand. Though some be so fell to meward, yet it goes not to the heart. All the council shall conclude much by me. Where great courts be gathered of kings or of great lords whereas need subtle counsel, there must Reynard find the subtle means. They may well speak and say their advice, but the mine is best and that goes tofore all other. In the court be many that have sworn to do me the worst they can and that causes me a part to be heavy in my heart, for many may do more than one alone that shall hurt me. Nevertheless, nephew, it is better I go with you to the court and answer for myself than to set me, my wife, and my children in a venture for to be lost. Arise up, let us go hence. He is over mighty for me. I must do as he wills. I cannot better it. I shall take it patiently and suffer it."

Reynard said to his wife, "Dame Ermelin, I betake you my children that you see well to them and specially to Reynkin,[71] my youngest son. He belikes me so well, I hope he shall follow my steps. And there is Rossel,[72] a passing fair thief. I love him as well as any may love his children. If God give me grace that I may escape, I shall when I come again thank you with fair words." Thus took Reynard leave of his wife.

Ah gods, how sorrowful abode Ermelin with her small whelps, for the victualler and he that sorrowed [73] for Maleperduys was gone his way and the house not purveyed nor victualled!

xii. *How Reynard Shrived Him*

When Reynard and Grimbert had gone a while together, tho said Reynard, "Dear cousin, now am I in great fear for I

belikes: resembles   *sorrowed*: provided

go in dread and jeopardy of my life. I have so much repentance for my sins that I will shrive me, dear cousin, to you. Here is no other priest to get. If I were shriven of my sins, my soul should be the clearer."

Grimbert answered, "Eme, will you shrive you, then must you promise first to leave your stealing and roving."

Reynard said that wist he well. "Now hark, dear cousin, what I shall say. Confiteor tibi pater [74] of all the misdeeds that I have done and gladly will receive penance for them."

Grimbert said, "What say you? Will you shrive you, then say it in English [75] that I may understand you."

Reynard said, "I have trespassed against all the beasts that live, in especial against Bruin the bear, my eme, whom I made his crown all bloody; and taught Tibert the cat to catch mice, for I made her [76] leap in a grin where she was all tobeaten. Also I have trespassed greatly against Chanticleer with his children, for I have made him quit of a great deal of them.

"The king is not gone all quit. I have slandered him and the queen many times that they shall never be clear thereof. Yet have I beguiled Isegrim the wolf oftener than I can tell well. I called him eme, but that was to deceive him. He is nothing of my kin. I made him a monk at Elmare,[77] where I myself also became one, and that was to his hurt and no profit. I made bind his feet to the bellrope. The ringing of the bell thought him so good that he would learn to ring, whereof he had shame. For he rang so sore that all the folk in the street were afraid thereof and marvelled what might be on the bell and ran thither tofore he had come to ask the religion, wherefore he was beaten almost to the death. After this I taught him to catch fish, where he received many a stroke. Also I lead him to the richest priest's house that was in Vermedos.[78] This

roving: plundering

7 2

priest had a spind wherein hung many a good flitch of bacon, wherein many a time I was wont to fill my belly. In this spind I had made a hole in which I made Isegrim to creep. There found he tubs with beef and many good flitches of bacon, whereof he ate so much without measure that he might not come out of the hole where he went in, his belly was so great and full of the meat and when he entered his belly was small. I went into the village and made there a great shout and noise. Yet hark what I did then! I ran to the priest where he sat at the table and ate and had tofore him as fat capon as a man might find. This capon caught I and ran my way therewith all that I might. The priest cried out and said, 'Take and slay the fox! I trow that never man saw more wonder. The fox cometh in my house and takes my capon from my table! Where saw ever man a hardier thief!' And as me thought, he took his table knife and cast it at me, but he touched me not. I ran away. He shoved the table from him and followed me crying, 'Kill and slay him!' I to go and they after and many more came after which all thought to hurt me. I ran so long that I came whereas Isegrim was; and there I let fall the capon, for it was too heavy for me and against my will I left it there and then I sprang through a hole whereas I would be. And as the priest took up the capon, he espied Isegrim and cried, 'Smite down here, friends! Here is the thief, the wolf! See well to that he escape us not!' They ran all together with stocks and staves and made a great noise that all the neighbors came out and gave him many a shrewd stroke and threw at him great stones in such wise that he fell down as he had been dead. They slepped him and drew him over stones and over blocks without the village and threw him into a ditch and there he lay all the night. I wot never how he came thence. Sith, I

spind: pantry   *slepped*: dragged   *wot*: know
sith: afterwards

73

have gotten of him, for as much as I made him to fill his belly, that he swore that he would be my help a whole year.

"Tho led I him to a place where I told him there were seven hens and a cock which sat on a perch and were much fat and there stood a falldoor by and we climbed thereup. I said to him if he would believe me and that he would creep into the door, he should find many fat hens. Isegrim went all laughing to the doorward and crept a little in and tasted here and there and at last he said to me, 'Reynard, you bourd and jape with me, for what I seek I find not.' Then said I, 'Eme, if you will find, creep further in. He that will win, he must labor and adventure. They that were wont to sit there, I have them away.' Thus I made him to seek further in and shoved him forth so far that he fell down upon the floor, for the perch was narrow and he fell so great a fall that they sprang up, all that slept, and they that lay next the fire cried that the falldoor was open and something was fallen and they wist not what it might be. They rose up and lit a candle and when they saw him, they smote, beat, and wounded him to the death.

"I have brought him thus in many a jeopardy more than I can now reckon. I should find many more if I me well bethought, which I shall tell you hereafter. Also I have bedriven with Dame Erswind [79] his wife. I would I had not done it. I am sorry for it. It is to her great shame and that me repents."

Grimbert said, "Eme, I understand you not?"

He said, "I have trespassed with his wife."

"You shrive you as though you held somewhat behind. I wot not what you mean nor where you have learned this language."

"Ach, dear eme, it were great shame if I should say it openly as it happed. I have laid by my aunt. I am your eme. I should

falldoor: trap door   tasted: felt   bourd: joke
bedriven: carried on

anger you if I spoke villainy of women. Nephew, now have I told you all that I can think on. Set me penance and assoil me for I have great repentance."

Grimbert saw his manner and said, "Foul false deceiver! How go your eyes so after the poultry!"

Grimbert was subtle and wise. He broke a rod off a tree and said, "Eme, now shall you smite yourself thrice with this rod on your body and then lay it down upon the ground and spring three times thereover without bowing of your legs and without stumbling and then shall you take it up and kiss it

assoil: absolve

75

friendly in token of meekness and obedience of your penance that I gave you. Herewith be you quit of all sins that you have done to this day for I forgive you all." The fox was glad.

Tho said Grimbert to his eme, "Eme, see now forthon that you do good works, read your psalms, go to church, fast, and keep your holidays, and give your alms and leave your sinful and ill life, your theft, and your treason and so may you come to mercy." The fox promised that he would so do, and then went they both together to the courtyard.

A little beside the way as they went stood a cloister of black nuns, where many geese, hens, and capons went without the walls. And as they went talking, the fox brought Grimbert out of the right way thither; and without the walls by the barn went the poultry. The fox espied them and saw a fat young capon which went along from his fellows and lept and caught him that the feathers flew around his ears. But the capon escaped.

Grimbert said, "What, eme! Cursed man, what will you do! Will you for one of these pullets fall again in all your sins, of which you have shriven you? You ought sore repent you."

Reynard answered, "Truly, cousin, I had all forgotten! Pray God that He forgive it me, for I will never do so more."

Then turned they again over a little bridge, yet the fox always looked after the poultry. He could not refrain himself. That which cleaved by the bone might not out of [80] the flesh. Though he should be hanged, he could not let the looking after the poultry as far as he might see them.

Grimbert saw his manner and said, "Foul false deceiver! How go your eyes so after the poultry!'

The fox said, "Cousin, you misdo to say to me any such words. You bring me out of my devotion and prayers. Let me say a pater noster for all the souls of the poultry and geese that I have betrayed and oft with falsehood stolen from these holy nuns."

Grimbert was not well apaid, but the fox had ever his eyes toward the poultry till at last they came in the way again. And then turned they to the courtward. How sore quaked tho Reynard when they approached the court, for he wist well that he had for to answer to many a foul feat and theft that he had done.

XIII. *How the Fox Came to the Court and How He Excused Him Tofore the King*

At the first when it was known in the court that Reynard the fox and Grimbert his cousin were come to the court, there was none so poor nor so feeble of kin and friends but that he made him ready for to complain on Reynard the fox.

Reynard looked as he had not been afraid and held him better than he was, for he went forth proudly with his nephew through the highest street of the court right as he had been the king's son and as he had not trespassed to any man the value of a hair and went in the middle of the place standing tofore Noble [81] the king and said, "God give you great honor and worship! There was never king that ever had a truer servant than I have been to your good grace and yet am. Nevertheless, dear lord, I know well that there be many in this court that would destroy me if you would believe them. But nay, God thank you, it is not fitting to your crown to believe these false deceivers and liars lightly. To God mote it be complained how that these false liars and flatterers nowadays in the lords' courts be most heard and believed. The shrews and false deceivers be borne up for to do to good men all the harm and scathe they may. Our Lord God shall once reward them their hire."

mote: must

The king said, "Reynard, false thief and traitor, how well can you bring forth fair tales! And all shall not help you a straw! Ween you with such flattering words to be my friend? You have so oft served me so as you now shall well know. The peace that I have commanded and sworn, that have you well held, have you?"

Chanticleer could no longer be still, but cried, "Alas, what have I by this peace lost!"

"Be still, Chanticleer, hold your mouth! Let me answer this false thief! Thou shrewd fell thief," said the king, "you say that you love me well? That have you showed well on my messengers, these poor fellows, Tibert the cat and Bruin the bear, which yet be all bloody, which chide not nor say not much, but that shall this day cost you your life. In nomine Pater Christe Filii!" [82]

Said the fox, "Dear lord and mighty king, if Bruin's crown be bloody, what is that to me? When he ate honey at Lantfert's house in the village and did him hurt and scathe, there was he beaten therefor. If he had willed, he is so strong of limb, he might well have been avenged ere he sprang into the water. Tho came Tibert the cat, whom I received friendly. If he went out without my counsel for to steal mice to a priest's house and the priest did him harm, should I aby that? Then might I say I were not happy. No so, my liege lord! You may do what you will though my matter be clear and good. You may seethe me or roast, hang, or make me blind. I may not escape you. We stand all under your correction. You be mighty and strong. I am feeble and my help is but small. If you put me to death, it were a small vengeance."

While they thus spoke, sprang up Bellin [83] the ram and his ewe, Dame Olewey,[84] and said, "My lord the king, hear our

seethe: boil

complaint!" Bruin the bear stood up with all his lineage and fellows. Tibert the cat. Isegrim the wolf. Cuwart the hare. And panther, the boar, the camel, and Brunel [85] the goose, the kid and goat, Boudewin [86] the ass, Borre [87] the bull, Hamel [88] the ox, and the weasel. Chanticleer the cock; Pertilot [89] with all her children. All these made great rumor and noise and came forth openly tofore their lord the king. And made that the fox was taken and arrested.

xiv. How the Fox Was Arrested and Judged to Death

Hereupon was a parliament and they decided that Reynard should be dead and whatsomever they said against the fox, he answered to each to them. Never heard man of such beasts, such plaints of wise counsel, and subtle inventions; and on the other side, the fox made his excuses so well and so formably thereon that they that heard it wondered thereof. They that heard and saw it may tell it for truth. I shall short the matter and tell you forth of the fox.

The king and the council heard the witnesses of the complaints of Reynard's misdeeds. It went with him as it oft does. The feeblest has the worst. They gave sentence and judged that the fox should be dead and hanged by the neck. Tho list he not to play. All his flattering words and deceits could not help him. The judgment was given and that must be. Dan Grimbert, his nephew, and many of his lineage might not find in their hearts to see him die, but took leave sorrowfully and roomed the court.

The king bethought him and marked how many a youngling departed from thence all weeping which were nigh of his kin and said to himself, "Here behooves other counsel hereto.

formably: elegantly   *list*: desired   *Dan*: Sir
roomed: left

79

Though Reynard be a shrew there be many good of his lineage."

Tibert the cat said, "Sir Bruin and Sir Isegrim, how be you thus slow! It is almost even. Here be many bushes and hedges. If he escaped from us and were delivered out of this peril, he is so subtle and so wily and can so many deceits that he should never be taken again. Shall we hang him? How stand you all thus? Ere the gallows can be made ready, it shall be night."

Isegrim bethought him tho and said, "Hereby is a gibbet or gallows." And with that word he sighed.

And the cat espied that and said, "Isegrim, you are afraid. Is it against your will? Think you not that he himself went and labored that both your brethren were hanged? Were you good and wise, you should thank him and you should not therewith so long tarry."

xv. *How the Fox Was Led to the Gallows*

Isegrim balked [90] and said, "You make much ado, Sir Tibert. Had we a halter which were meet for his neck and strong enough, we should soon make an end."

Reynard the fox, which long had not spoken, said to Isegrim, "Short my pain! Tibert hath a strong cord which caught him in the priest's house when he bit off the priest's genitors. He can climb well and is swift. Let him bear up the line. Isegrim and Bruin, this becomes you well that you thus do to your nephew. I am sorry that I lived thus long. Haste you! You be set thereto. It is evil done that you tarry thus long. Go tofore, Bruin, and lead me. Isegrim, follow fast and see well to and beware that Reynard go not away."

Tho said Bruin, "It is the best counsel that I ever heard that Reynard said."

can: knows   *genitors*: genitals

Isegrim commanded anon and bade his kin and friends that they should see to Reynard that he escaped not, for he is so wily and false. They held him by the feet, by the beard, and so kept him that he escaped not from them.

The fox heard all these words which touched him nigh; yet spoke he and said, "Och, dear eme, methinks you pain yourself sore for to do me hurt and scathe. If I dared, I would pay you of mercy,[91] though my hurt and sorrow is pleasant to you. I wot well if my aunt, your wife, bethought her well of old ferners, she would not suffer that I should have any harm. But now I am he that now you will do on me what it shall please you. You, Bruin and Tibert, God give you shame's death but you do to me your worst. I wot whereto I shall. I may die but once. I would that I were dead already. I saw my father die; he had soon done."

Isegrim said, "Let us go, for you curse us because we lengthen the time. Evil mote he fare if we abide any longer."

He went forth with great envy on that one side and Bruin stood on the other side and so led they him forth to the gallowsward. Tibert ran with a good will tofore and bore the cord and his throat was yet sore of the grin and his crop did him woe of the strike that he was taken in; that happed by the counsel of the fox and that thought he now to quit.

Tibert, Isegrim, and Bruin went hastily with Reynard to the place thereas the felons be wont to be put to death. Noble the king and the queen and all that were in the court followed after for to see the end of Reynard. The fox was in great dread if him mishapped and bethought him oft how he might save him from the death; and those three that so desired his death, how he might deceive them and bring them to shame; and how he might bring the king with lesings for to hold with him

ferners: times   mote: may   strike: snare
quit: repay   lesings: deceits

81

against them. This was all that he studied: how he might put away his sorrow with wiles. And thought, "Thus though the king and many one be upon me angry, it is no wonder for I have well deserved it. Nevertheless, I hope for to be yet their best friend and yet shall I never do them good. How strong that the king be and how wise that his counsel be, if I may brook my words, I know so many an invention I shall come to my above as far as they would come to the gallows." [92]

Tho said Isegrim, "Sir Bruin, think now on your red crown, which by Reynard's means you caught. We have now the time that we may well reward him. Tibert, climb up hastily and bind the cord fast to the linden and make a riding knot or strop. You be the lightest. You shall this day see your will of him. Bruin, see well to that he escape not and hold fast. I will help that the ladder be set up that he may go upward thereon."

Bruin said, "Do, I shall help him well."

The fox said, "Now may my heart be well heavy for great dread, for I see the death tofore my eyes and I may not escape. My lord the king and dear queen and forth all you that stand here, ere I depart from this world I pray of you a boon that I may tofore you all make my confession openly and tell my default all so clearly that my soul be not encumbered and also that no man hereafter bear no blame for my theft nor for my treason. My death shall be to me the easier and pray you all to God that He have mercy on my soul."

XVI. *How the Fox Made Openly His Confession Tofore the King and Tofore All Them That Would Hear It*

All they that stood there had pity when Reynard said those words and said it was but a little request if the king

brook: use   *strop*: loop   *forth*: further

82

would grant it him and they prayed the king to grant it him. The king gave him leave. Reynard was glad and hoped that it might fall better and said thus:

"Now help Spiritus Domini for I see here no man but I have trespassed unto. Nevertheless, yet was I unto the time that I was weaned from the teat one the best child that could anywhere be found. I went tho and played with the lambs because I heard them gladly bleat. I was so long with them that at last I bit one. There learned I first to lap of the blood. It savored well. Methought it right good. And after I began to taste of the flesh thereof, I was lickerous so that after that I went to the goats into the wood. There heard I the kids bleat and I slew of them twain. I began to wax hardy. After, I slew hens, poultry, and geese wherever I found them. Thus worden my teeth all bloody. After this I waxed so fell and so wroth that whatsomever I found that I might over,[93] I slew all.

"Thereafter came I by Isegrim now in the winter where he hid him under a tree and reckoned to me that he was my eme. When I heard him then reckon alliance, we became fellows, which I may well repent. We promised each to other to be true and to use good fellowship and began to wander together. He stole the great things and I the small and always common between us. Yet he made it so that he had the best deal. I got not half my part. When that Isegrim got a calf, a ram, or a wither, then grimmed he and was angry on me and drove me from him and held my part and his too. So good is he!

"Yet this was of the least. But when it so lucked that we took an ox or a cow, then came thereto his wife with seven children so that unto me might uneath come one of the smallest ribs, and yet had they eaten all the flesh thereof. Therewithal must I be content, not for that I had great need, for I have so

lickerous: greedy   *worden*: became   *grimmed*: grew angry great scat[94] and good of silver and of gold that seven wains should not con carry it away."

When the king heard him speak of this great good and richess, he burned in the desire and covetousness thereof and said, "Reynard, where is the richess become? Tell me that?"

The fox said, "My lord, I shall tell you. The richess was stolen and had it not been stolen, it should have cost you your life and should have been murdered, which God forbid and should have been the greatest hurt of the world."

When the queen heard that she was sore afraid and cried aloud, "Alas and wellaway! Reynard, what say you? I conjure you by the long way that your soul shall go that you tell us openly the truth hereof as much as you know of this great murder that should have been done on my lord that we all may hear it."

Now harken how the fox shall flatter the king and queen and shall win both their good will and love and shall hinder them that labor for his death. He shall unbind his pack and lie and by flattery and fair words shall bring forth so his matters that it shall be supposed for truth.

In a sorrowful countenance spoke the fox to the queen, "I am in such case now that I must needs die and had you me not so sore conjured, I will not jeopardy my soul; and if I so die, I should go therefore into the pain of hell. I will say nothing but that I will make it good. For piteously he should have been murdered of his own folk. Nevertheless, they that were most principal in this feat were of my next kin, whom gladly I would not bewray if the sorrow were not of the hell."

The king was heavy of heart and said, "Reynard, say you to me the truth?"

"Yea," said the fox, "see you not how it stands with me?

scat: treasure   *conjure*: implore   *bewray*: expose

Ween you that I will damn my soul? What should it avail me if I now said otherwise than truth? My death is so nigh. There may neither prayer nor good help me." Tho trembled the fox by dissimulating as he had been afraid.

The queen had pity on him and prayed the king to have mercy on him in eschewing of more harm [95] and that he should do the people hold their peace and give the fox audience and hear what he should say. Tho commanded the king openly that each of them should be still and suffer the fox to say unberisped what that he would.

Then said the fox, "Be you now all still sith it is the king's will and I shall tell you openly this treason and therein I will spare no man that I know guilty."

XVII. *How the Fox Brought Them in Danger That Would Have Brought Him to Death and How He Got the Grace of the King*

Now harken how the fox began. In the beginning he appealed Grimbert his cousin, which ever had helped him in his need. He did so because his words should be the better believed and that he forthon might the better lie on his enemies. Thus began he first and said:

"My lord, my father had found King Ermerik's [96] treasure delved in a pit; and when he had this great good he was so proud and orgulous that he had all other beasts in despite which tofore had been his fellows. He made Tibert the cat to go into the wild land of Ardennes to Bruin the bear for to do to him homage and bade him say if he would be king that he should come into Flanders. Bruin the bear was glad hereof for he had long desired it and went forth into Flanders where my father received him right friendly. Anon he sent for the wise Grim-

unberisped: undisturbed   *appealed*: accused   *delved*: buried
orgulous: haughty   *despite*: contempt

85

bert, my nephew, and for Isegrim the wolf and for Tibert the cat. Tho these five came between Ghent and the thorpe called Ifte.[97] There they held their council a whole dark night long. What with the devil's help and craft and for my father's richess, they concluded and swore there the king's death.

"Now harken and hear this wonder! The four swore upon Isegrim's crown [98] that they should make Bruin a king and a lord and bring him in the stool at Aachen and set the crown on his head and if there were any of the king's friends or lineage that would be contrary or against this, him should my father with his good and treasure fordrive and take from his might and power.

"It happed so that on a morrowtide early that Grimbert, my nephew, was of wine almost drunk that he told it to Dame Slopecade,[99] his wife, in counsel and bade her keep it secret. But she anon forgot it and said it forth in confession to my wife upon a heath where they both went a pilgrimage. But she must first swear by her truth and by the holy three kings of Cologne [100] that for love nor for hate she should never tell it forth, but keep it secret. But she held it not and kept it no longer secret but till she came to me and she then told it to me, all that she heard. But I must keep it in secret and she told me so many tokens that I felt well it was truth and for dread and fear my hair stood right up and my heart became as heavy as lead and as cold as ice.

"I thought by this a likeness which here aforetime befell to the frogs, which were free and complained that they had no lord nor were not bedwongen.[101] For a community without a governor was not good and they cried to God with a loud voice that he would ordain one that might rule them. This was

stool: throne	*fordrive*: drive away	*morrowtide*: morning-
tokens: details	*likeness*: parable	tide
bedwongen: governed		

all they desired. God heard their request, for it was reasonable, and sent to them a stork which ate and swallowed them in, as many as he could find. He was always to them unmerciful. Tho complained they their hurt, but then it was too late. They that were tofore free and were afraid of nobody be now bond and must obey to strength their king.[102] Herefore, you rich and poor, I sorrowed that it might happen us in like wise.

"Thus, my lord the king, I have had sorrow for you, whereof you can me but little thank.[103] I know Bruin the bear for such a shrew and ravener wherefore I thought if he were king, we should be all destroyed and lost. I know our sovereign lord the king of so high birth, so mighty, so benign and merciful that I thought truly it had been an evil change for to have a foul stinking thief and to refuse a noble mighty stately lion. For the bear has more mad folly in his unthrifty head and all his ancestors than any other has. Thus had I in my heart many a sorrow and thought always how I might break and fordo my father's false counsel, which of a churl and a traitor and worse than a thief would make a lord and a king. Always I prayed God that he would keep our king in worship and good health and grant him long life. But I thought well if my father held his treasure he should with his false fellows well find the way that the king should be deposed and set aside. I was sore bethought how I might best wit where my father's good lay. I awaited at all times as nigh as I could in woods, in bushes, in fields, where my father laid his eyes, were it by night, or by day, cold or wet. I was always by him to espy and know where his treasure was laid.

"On a time I lay down all plat on the ground and saw my father come running out of a hole. Now hark what I saw him do! When he came out of the hole, he looked fast about if

herefore: therefor   *ravener*: plunderer   *fordo*: thwart
plat: flat

anybody had seen him. And when he could no one see, he stopped the hole with sand and made it even and plain like to the other ground by. He knew not that I saw him and where his footspoor stood. There struck he with his tail and made it smooth with his mouth that no man should espy it. That learned I there of my false father and many subtleties that I tofore knew nothing of. Then departed he thence and ran to the villageward for to do his things. And I forgot not but sprang and lept to the holeward; and how well that he had supposed that he had made all fast, I was not so much a fool but that I found the hole well and cratched and scraped with my feet the sand out of the hole and crept therein.

"There found I the most plenty of silver and gold that ever I saw. Here is none so old that ever so much saw on one heap in all his life. Tho took I Ermelin, my wife, to help and we neither rested night nor day to bear and carry away with great labor and pain this rich treasure into another place that lay for us better under a haw in a deep hole. In the meanwhile that my housewife and I thus labored, my father was with them that would betray the king. Now may you hear what they did! Bruin the bear and Isegrim the wolf sent all the land about if any man would take wages that they should come to Bruin and he would pay them their sold or wages tofore. My father ran all over the land and bore the letters. He wist little that he was robbed of his treasure. Yea, tho he might have won all the world, he had not con find a penny thereof.

"When my father had been over all in the land between the Elbe and the Somme [104] and had gotten many a soldier that should the next summer have come to help Bruin, tho came he again to the bear and his fellows and told them in how great a venture he had been tofore the burgs in the land of Saxony [105]

cratched: scratched   *haw*: hedge   *sold*: hire

88

and how the hunters daily rode and hunted with hounds after him in such wise that he uneath escaped with his life. When he had told this to these four false traitors, then showed he them letters that pleased much to Bruin. Therein were written 1200 of Isegrim's lineage without the bear's, the fox's, the cat's, and the dasse's. All these had sworn that with the first messenger that should come for them, they should be ready and come forth to help the bear, if they had their wages a month tofore. This espied I, I thank God! After these words my father went to the hole where his treasure had lain and would look upon it. Tho began he a great sorrow. That he sought, he found nothing. He found his hole broken and his treasure borne away. There did he that I may well sorrow and bewail for great anger and sorrow. He went and hanged himself. Thus abode the treason of Bruin by my subtlety after.[106]

"Now see my infortune! These traitors Isegrim and Bruin be now most privy of council about the king and sit by him on the high bouche [107] and I, poor Reynard, have no thank nor reward! I have buried my own father because the king should have his life.

"My lord," said the fox, "where be they that so would do, that is, to destroy themselves for to keep you?"

The king and the queen hoped to win the treasure and without counsel took to them Reynard and prayed him that he would do so well as to tell them where this treasure was.

Reynard said, "How should I tell the king or them that would hang me? For love of the traitors and murderers which by their flattery would fain bring me to death? Should I tell to them where my good is? Then were I out of my wit!"

The queen tho spoke, "Nay, Reynard, the king shall let you have your life and shall altogether forgive you and you shall be from henceforth wise and true to my lord!"

The fox answered to the queen, "Dear lady, if the king will believe me and that he will pardon and forgive me all my old trespasses, there was never king so rich as I shall make him. For the treasure that I shall do him have is right costly and may not be numbered."

The king said, "Ach, dame, will you believe the fox? Save your reverence, he is born to rob, steal and to lie. This cleaved to his bones and can not be had out of the flesh."

The queen said, "Nay, my lord, you may now well believe him. Tho he were tofore fell, he is now changed otherwise than he was. You have well heard that he has appeached his father and the dasse, his nephew, which he might well have laid on other beasts if he would have been false, fell, and a liar."

The king said, "Dame, will you then have it so and think you it best to be done, tho I supposed it should hurt me, I will take all these trespasses of Reynard upon me and believe his words. If he ever hereafter misdo and trespass that shall he dear aby and all his lineage unto the ninth degree." [108] The fox looked on the king stoundmeal and was glad in his heart and said, "My lord, I were not wise if I should say things that were not true."

The king took up a straw [109] from the ground and pardoned and forgave the fox all the misdeeds and trespasses of his father and of him also. If the fox was tho merry and glad, it was no wonder for he was quit of his death and was all free and frank of all his enemies.

The fox said, "My lord the king and noble lady the queen, God reward you this great worship that you do to me! I shall think and also thank you for it in such wise that you shall be the richest king of the world, for there is none living

appeached: accused   *stoundmeal*: at intervals   *frank*: clear under the sun that I vouchsafe better my treasure on than on you both."

Then took the fox up a straw and proffered it to the king and said, "My most dear lord, please it you to receive here the rich treasure which King Ermerik had, for I give it unto you with a free will and knowledge it openly." The king received the straw and threw it merrily from him with a joyous visage and thanked much the fox. The fox laughed in himself. The king then harkened after the counsel of the fox. And all that there were, were at his will.

"My lord," said he, "harken and mark well my words! In the west side of Flanders there stands a wood and is named Hulsterloo [110] and a water that is called Krekenpit [111] lies thereby. This is so great a wilderness that oft in a whole year man nor wife comes therein save they that will and they that will not eschew it. There lies this treasure hid. Understand well that the place is called Krekenpit, for I advise you for the least hurt that you and my lady go both thither. For I know none so true that I dared on your behalf trust; wherefore go yourself. And when you come to Krekenpit, you shall find there two birch trees standing all there next the pit. My lord, to those birch trees shall you go. There lies the treasure underdelved. There must you scrape and dig away a little the moss on the one side. There shall you find many a jewel of gold and silver and there shall you find the crown which King Ermerik wore in his day, that should Bruin the bear have worn if his will had gone forth. You shall see many a costly jewel with rich stone set in gold work which cost many a thousand mark. My lord the king, when you now have all this good, how oft shall you say in your heart and think, 'Oh how true are you, Reynard the fox, that with your subtle wit delved and hid

underdelved: buried
thereunder

here this great treasure! God give you good hap and welfare wherever you be!' "

The king said, "Sir Reynard, you must come and help us to dig up this treasure. I know not the way. I should never con find it. I have heard oft named Paris, London, Aachen, and Cologne. As methinks, this treasure lies right as you mocked and japed, for you named Krekenpit. That is a famed name!"

These words were not good to the fox and he said with an angry mood and dissimulated and said, "You, my lord the king, you be also nigh that as from Rome to May! [112] Ween you that I will lead you to Flume Jordan? Nay, I shall bring you out of weening and show it you by good witness."

He called loud, "Cuwart the hare! Come here tofore the king!" The beasts saw all thitherward and wondered what the king would.

The fox said to the hare, "Cuwart, are you acold? How tremble you and quake so! Be not afraid and tell my lord the king here the truth and that I charge you by the faith in truth that you owe him and to my lady the queen of such things as I shall demand of you."

Cuwart said, "I shall say the truth though I should lose my neck therefor! I shall not lie, you have charged me so sore, if I know it!"

"Then say know you not where Krenkenpit stands? Is that in your mind?"

The hare said, "I knew that well twelve years ago where that stood. Why ask you that? It stood in a wood named Hulsterloo upon a warren in the wilderness. I have suffered there much sorrow for hunger and for cold. Yea, more than I can tell! Pater Simonet, the Friesian,[113] was wont to make there false money, wherewith he bore himself out and all

famed: imaginary   *flume*: river

92

his fellowship. But that was tofore ere I had fellowship with Rine [114] the hound, which made me escape many a danger, as he could well tell if he were here and that I never in my days trespassed against the king otherwise than I ought to do with right."

Reynard said to him, "Go again to yonder fellowship! Hear you, Cuwart, my lord the king desires no more to know of you." The hare returned and went again to the place he came from.

The fox said, "My lord the king, is it true that I said?"

"Yea, Reynard," said the king, "forgive it me! I did evil that I believed you not. Now, Reynard friend, find the way, that you go with us to the place and pit where the treasure lies."

The fox said, "It is a wonder thing! Ween you that I would not fain go with you, if it were so with me that I might go with you in such wise that it no shame were unto your lordship? I would go; but nay, it may not be. Harken what I shall say and must needs, though it be to me villainy and shame. When Isegrim the wolf in the devil's name went into religion and became a monk shorn in the order, tho the provender of six monks was not sufficient to him and had not enough to eat, he then plained and wailed so sore, that I had pity on him. For he became slow and sick; and because he was of my kin, I gave him counsel to run away and so he did, wherefore I stand accursed and am in the Pope's ban and sentence. I will tomorrow betimes as the sun rises take my way to Rome for to be assoiled and take pardon and from Rome I will over the sea into the Holy Land and will never return again till I have done so much good that I may with worship go with you. It were great reproof to you, my lord the king, in what land that

betimes: early

93

I accompanied you that men should say you rised and accompanied yourself with a cursed and a person aggravate."

The king said, "Sith that you stand accursed in the censures of the church, if I went with you men should arette villainy unto my crown. I shall then take Cuwart or some other to go with me to Krekenpit and I counsel you, Reynard, that you put yourself out of this curse."

"My lord," quod the fox, "therefore will I go to Rome as hastily as I may. I shall not rest by night nor day till I be assoiled."

"Reynard," said the king, "methinks you be turned into a good way. God give you grace to accomplish well your desire."

As soon as this speaking was done, Noble the king went and stood upon a high stage of stone and commanded silence to all the beasts and that they should sit down in a ring round upon the grass, everyone in his place after his estate and birth. Reynard the fox stood by the queen, whom he ought well to love.

Then said the king, "Hear you, all that be poor and rich, young and old, that stand here! Reynard, one of the head officers of my house, had done so evil, which this day should have been hanged, has now in this court done so much that I and my wife the queen have promised to him our grace and friendship. The queen has prayed much for him insomuch that I have made peace with him and I give to him his life and member freely again and I command you upon your life that you do worship to Reynard, his wife, and to his children, wheresomever you meet them by day or night. And I will also hear no more complaints of Reynard. If he has heretofore mis-

rised: traveled   *aggravate*: excommuni-   *arette*: ascribe
member: limb   cated

done and trespassed, he will no more misdo nor trespass, but now better him. He will tomorrow early go to the Pope for pardon and forgiveness of all his sins and forth over the sea to the Holy Land. And he will not come again till he bring pardon of all his sins."

This tale heard Tiselin [115] the raven and lept to Isegrim, to Bruin, and to Tibert, there as they were and said, "You caitiffs, how goes it now? You unhappy folk, what do you here? Reynard the fox is now a squire and a courtier and right great and mighty in the court. The king has skilled him quit of all his brokes and forgiven him all his trespasses and misdeeds and you are all betrayed and appeached."

Isegrim said, "How may this be? I trow Tiselin that you lie!"

"I do not certainly," said the raven.

Tho went the wolf and the bear to the king. Tibert the cat was in great sorrow. He was so sore afraid that for to have the fox's friendship, he would well forgive Reynard the loss of his one eye that he lost in the priest's house. He was so woe he wist not what to do. He would well that he never had seen the fox.

XVIII. *How the Wolf and the Bear Were Arrested by the Labor of Reynard the Fox*

Isegrim came proudly over the field tofore the king and he thanked the queen and spoke with a fell mood ill words on the fox in such wise that the king heard it and was wroth and made the wolf and the bear anon to be arrested. You saw never wood dogs do more harm than was done to them that were both fast bound so sore that all that night they might not stir hand nor foot. They might scarcely rore nor move any joint.

skilled: judged   *brokes*: transgressions   *wood*: mad
rore: stir

Now hear how the fox forth did. He hated them. He labored so to the queen that he got leave for to have as much of the bear's skin upon his ridge as a foot long and a foot broad for to make him thereof a scrip. Then was the fox ready if he had four strong shoes. Now hear how he did for to get these shoes.

He said to the queen, "Madame, I am your pilgrim. Here is my eme, Sir Isegrim, that has four strong shoes which were good for me. If he would let me have two of them, I would on the way busily think on your soul; for it is right that a pilgrim should always think and pray for them that do him good. Thus may you do your soul good if you will. And also if you might get of my aunt, Dame Erswind, also two of her shoes to give me, she may well do it for she goes but little out, but abides always at home."

Then said the queen, "Reynard, you behoove well such shoes. You may not be without them. They shall be good for you to keep your feet whole for to pass with them many a sharp mountain and stony rocks. You can find no better shoes for you such as Isegrim and his wife have. And where they be good and strong, though it should touch their life, each of them shall give you two shoes for to accomplish with your high pilgrimage.

XIX. *How Isegrim and His Wife Erswind Must Suffer Their Shoes to Be Plucked Off and How Reynard Did on the Shoes for to Go to Rome With*

Thus has this false pilgrim gotten from Isegrim two shoes from his feet, which were hauled off the claws to the sinews. You saw never fowl that men roasted lie so still as Isegrim did when his shoes were hauled off. He stirred not and yet his feet bled. Then when Isegrim was unshod, tho must Dame Ers-

ridge: back   *scrip*: wallet

wind, his wife, lie down in the grass with a heavy cheer and she lost her hinder shoes.

Tho was the fox glad and said to his aunt in scorn, "My dear aunt, how much sorrow have you suffered for my sake, which me sore repents; save this, hereof I am glad, for you be the liefest of all my kin. Therefore, I will gladly wear your shoes. You shall be partner of my pilgrimage and deal of the pardon that I shall with your shoes fetch over the sea."

Dame Erswind was so woe that she uneath might speak. Nevertheless, this she said, "Ah, Reynard, that you now all thus have your will, I pray God to wreak it!"

Isegrim and his fellow the bear held their peace and were all still. They were evil at ease, for they were bound and sore wounded. Had Tibert the cat have been there, he should also somewhat have suffered in such wise as he should not escape thence without hurt or shame.

The next day when the sun arose, Reynard then did grease his shoes, which he had of Isegrim and Erswind his wife, and did them on and bound them to his feet and went to the king and to the queen and said to them with a glad cheer, "Noble lord and lady, God give you good morrow and I desire of your grace that I have mail and staff blest as belong to a pilgrim." Then the king anon sent for Bellin the ram and when he came, he said, "Sir Bellin, you shall do mass tofore Reynard for he shall go on pilgrimage and give to him mail and staff."

The ram answered again and said, "My lord, I dare not do that for he has said that he is in the Pope's curse."

The king said, "What thereof? Master Gelys [116] has said to us, if a man had done as many sins as all the world and he would those sins forsake, shrive him and receive penance and do by the priest's counsel, God will forgive them and be

cheer: mien   *wreak*: avenge

merciful unto him. Now will Reynard go over the sea into the Holy Land and make him clear of all his sins."

Then answered Bellin to the king, "I will not do little nor much herein but if you save me harmless in the spiritual court before the Bishop Prendelor [117] and tofore his Archdeacon Loosefind [118] and tofore Sir Rapiamus,[119] his official."

The king began to wax wroth and said, "I shall not bid you so much in half a year! I had liefer hang you than I should so much pray you for it."

When the ram saw that the king was angry, he was so sore afraid that he quaked for fear and went to the altar and sang in his books and read such as him thought good over Reynard, which little set thereby save that he would have the worship thereof.

When Bellin the ram had all said his service devoutly, then he hung on the fox's neck a mail covered with the skin of Bruin the bear and a little palster thereby. Tho was Reynard ready toward his journey. Tho looked he toward the king as he had been sorrowful to depart and fained as he had wept right as he had yammered in his heart. But if he had any sorrow, it was because all the others that were there were not in the same plight as the wolf and bear were brought in by him. Nevertheless, he stood and prayed them all to pray for him like as he would pray for them. The fox thought that he tarried long and would fain have departed for he knew himself guilty.

The king said, "Reynard, I am sorry you be so hasty and will no longer tarry."

"Nay, my lord, it is time! For me ought not to spare to do well. I pray you to give me leave to depart. I must do my pilgrimage."

palster: pilgrim's staff   *yammered*: grieved

98

The king said, "God be with you!" And commanded all of them of the court to go and convey Reynard save the wolf and the bear, which fast lay bound. There was none that dared be sorry therefor. And if you had seen Reynard, how personably he went with his mail and palster on his shoulder, and the shoes on his feet, you should have laughed. He went and showed him outward wisely, but he laughed in his heart, that all they brought him forth which had a little tofore been with him so wroth and also the king, which so much hated him, he had made him such a fool that he brought him to his own intent. He was a pilgrim of deux as.[120]

"My lord the king," said the fox, "I pray you to return again. I will not that you go any further with me; you might have harm thereby. You have there two murderers arrested. If they escape you, you might be hurt by them. I pray God keep you from misadventure."

With these words he stood up on his after feet and prayed all the beasts, great and small, that would be partners of his pardon that they should pray for him. They said that they all would remember him. Then departed he from the king so heavily that many of them ermed.

Then said he to Cuwart the hare and to Bellin the ram merrily, "Dear friends, shall we now depart? You will and God will accompany me further. You two made me never angry. You be good for to walk with, courteous, friendly, and not complained on of any beast. You be of good condition and ghostly of your living. You live both as I did when I was a recluse. If you have any leaves and grass, you be pleased. You retch not of bread, of flesh, nor such manner meat."

With such flattering words has Reynard these two flattered that they went with him till they came tofore his house Maleperduys.

ermed: grieved   *retch*: care

99

xx. *How Cuwart the Hare Was Slain by the Fox*

When the fox was come tofore the gate of his house, he said to Bellin the ram, "Cousin, you shall abide here without. I and Cuwart will go in, for I will pray Cuwart to help me to take my leave of Ermelin, my wife, and to comfort her and my children."

Bellin said, "I pray him to comfort them well."

With such flattering words brought he the hare into his hole in an evil hour. There found they Dame Ermelin lying on the ground with her younglings, which had sorrowed much for dread of Reynard's death. But when she saw him come, she was glad; but when she saw his mail and palster and espied his shoes, she marvelled and said, "Dear Reynard, how have you sped?"

He said, "I was arrested in court, but the king let me go. I must go a pilgrimage. Bruin the bear and Isegrim the wolf, they be pledged for me. I thank the king. He has given to us Cuwart here for to do with him what we will. The king said himself that Cuwart was the first that on us complained; and by the faith that I owe you I am right wroth on Cuwart."

When Cuwart heard these words, he was sore afraid. He would have fled, but he might not for the fox stood between him and the gate. And he caught him by the neck.

Tho cried the hare, "Help, Bellin, help! Where be you? This pilgrim slays me!" But that cry was soon done, for the fox had anon bitten his throat atwo.

Tho said he, "Let us go eat this good fat hare." The young whelps came also. Thus held they a great feast, for Cuwart had a good fat body. Ermelin ate the flesh and drank the blood. She thanked oft the king that he had made them so merry. The fox said, "Eat as much as you may. He will pay for it if we fetch it." [121]

She said, "Reynard, I trow you mock! Tell me the truth how you departed thence?"

"Dame, I have so flattered the king and the queen that I suppose the friendship between us shall be right thin when he shall know of this. He shall be angry and hastily seek me for to hang me by the neck. Therefore let us depart and steal secretly away in some other forest where we may live without fear and dread and there that we may live seven year and more and find us not. There is plenty of good meat, of partridges, wododekkis,[122] and much other wild fowl. Dame, and if you will come with me thither, there be sweet wells and fair and clear running brooks. Lord God, how sweet air is there! There may we be in peace and ease and live in great wealth. For the king has let me go because I told him that there was great treasure in Krekenpit, but there he shall find nothing, tho he sought ever. This shall sore anger him when he knows that he is thus deceived. What trow you how many a great lesing must I lie ere I could escape from him. It was hard that I escaped out of prison. I was never in greater peril nor nearer my death. But how it ever go, I shall by my will never more come in the king's danger. I have now gotten my thumb out of his mouth. That thank I my subtlety."

Dame Ermelin said, "Reynard, I counsel that we go not into another forest where we should be strange and elenge.[123] We have here all that we desire and you be here lord of our neighbors. Wherefore shall we leave this place and adventure us in a worse? We may abide here sure enough. If the king would do us any harm or besiege us, here be so many by- or side holes in such wise as we shall escape from him. In abiding here, we may not do amiss. We know all bypaths overall; and ere he takes us with might, he must have much help thereto.

elenge: miserable

101

But that you have sworn that you shall go oversea and abide there, that is the thing that touches me most."

"Nay, dame, care not therefor! How more forsworn, how more forlorn. I went once with a good man that said to me that a bedwongen oath or oath sworn by force was no oath. Tho I went on his pilgrimage, it should not avail me a cat's tail. I will abide here and follow your counsel. If the king hunt after me, I shall keep me as well as I may. If he be me too mighty, yet I hope with subtlety to beguile him. I shall unbind my sack. If he will seek harm, he shall find harm."

Now was Bellin the ram angry that Cuwart his fellow was so long in the hole and called loud, "Come out, Cuwart, in the devil's name! How long shall Reynard keep you there? Haste you and come let us go!"

When Reynard heard this, he went out and said softly to Bellin the ram, "Lief Bellin, wherefore be you angry? Cuwart speaks with his dear aunt. Methinks you ought not to be displeased therefor. He bade me say to you 'You might well go tofore and he shall come after.' He is lighter of foot than you. He must tarry a while with his aunt and her children. They weep and cry because I shall go from them."

Bellin said, "What did Cuwart? Me thought he cried after help."

The fox answered, "What say you, Bellin? Ween you that he should have any harm? Now hark what he then did. When we were come into my house and Ermelin my wife understood that I should go oversea, she fell down in a swoon; and when Cuwart saw that, he cried loud 'Come help my aunt to bring her out of her swoon.'"

Then said the ram, "In faith, I understood that Cuwart had been in great danger."

bedwongen: compelled

The fox said, "Nay, truly, or Cuwart should have any harm in my house, I had liefer that my wife and children should suffer much hurt."

XXI. *How the Fox Sent the Head of Cuwart the Hare to the King by Bellin the Ram*

The fox said, "Bellin, remember you not that yesterday the king and his council commanded me that ere I should depart out of this land, I should send to him two letters. Dear cousin, I pray you to bear them. They be ready written."

Know not you how you misdealed on the plaice when he threw down from the car?

The ram said, "I wot never if I wist that your inditing and writing were good. You might peradventure so much pray me that I would bear them if I had anything to bear them in."

Reynard said, "You shall not fail to have somewhat to bear them in. Rather than they should be unborne, I shall rather give you my mail that I bear and put the king's letters therein and hang them around your neck. You shall have of the king great thank therefor and be right welcome to him." Hereupon Bellin promised him to bear these letters.

Tho returned Reynard into his house and took the mail and put therein Cuwart's head and brought it to Bellin for to bring him in danger and hung it on his neck and charged him not for to look in the mail, if he would have the king's friendship and "If you will that the king take you into his grace and love you, say that you yourself have made the letter and indited it and have given the counsel that it is so well made and written. You shall have great thanks therefor."

Bellin the ram was glad hereof and thought he should have great thank and said, "Reynard, I wot well that you now do for me. I shall be in the court greatly praised when it is known that I can so well indite and make a letter. Though I cannot make it, oftimes it haps that God suffers some to have worship and thank of the labors and cunning of other men and so it shall befall me now. Now what counsel you, Reynard? Shall Cuwart the hare come with me to the court?"

"Nay," said the fox, "he shall anon follow you. He may not yet come for he must speak with his aunt. Now go you forth tofore. I shall show to Cuwart secret things which be not yet known."

Bellin said, "Farewell, Reynard!" And went him forth to the court and he ran and hasted so fast that he came tofore midday to the court and found the king in his palace with his barons. The king marvelled when he saw him bring the mail again which was made of the bear's skin.

The king said, "Say on, Bellin, from whence come you? Where is the fox? How is it that he has not the mail with him?"

Bellin said, "My lord, I shall say you all that I know. I accompanied Reynard unto his house. And when he was ready, he asked me if I that would for your sake bear two letters to you. I said for to do you pleasure and worship I would gladly bear to you seven. Tho brought he to me this mail wherein the letters be which he indited by my cunning and I gave counsel of the making of them. I trow you saw never letters better nor craftlier made nor indited."

The king commanded anon Bokart,[124] his secretary, to read the letters for he understood all manner languages. Tibert the cat and he took the mail off Bellin's neck and Bellin has so far said and confessed that he therefore was damned.

The clerk Bokart undid the mail and drew out Cuwart's head and said, "Alas, what letters be these? Certainly, my lord, this is Cuwart's head!"

"Alas," said the king, "that ever I believed so the fox!" There might men see great heaviness of the king and of the queen. The king was so angry that he held long down his head and at last after many thoughts he made a great cry that all the beasts were afraid of the noise.

Tho spoke Sir Firapeel [125] the leopard, which was sib somewhat to the king and said, "Sir king, how make you such a noise? You make sorrow enough tho the queen were dead. Let this sorrow go and make good cheer. It is great shame! Be you not a lord and king of this land? Is it not all under you that here is?"

sib: kin

105

The king said, "Sir Firapeel, how should I suffer this? One false shrew and deceiver has betrayed me and brought me so far that I have forwrought and angered my friends, that I,[126] the stout Bruin the bear and Isegrim the wolf, which sore me repents. And this goes against my worship that I have done amiss against my best barons and that I trusted and believed so much the false whoreson, the fox; and my wife is cause thereof. She prayed me so much that I heard her prayer and that me repents though it be too late."

"What though, sir king," said the leopard, "if there be anything misdone, it shall be amended. We shall give to Bruin the bear, to Isegrim the wolf, and to Erswind his wife for the piece of his skin and for their shoes for to have good peace Bellin the ram. For he has confessed himself that he gave counsel and consented to Cuwart's death. It is reason that he aby it and we all shall go fetch Reynard and we shall arrest him and hang him by the neck without law or judgment and therewith all shall be content."

XXII. *How Bellin the Ram and All His Lineage Were Given in the Hands of Isegrim and Bruin and How He Was Slain*

The king said, "I will do it gladly."

Firapeel the leopard went tho to the prison and unbound them first and then he said, "You sirs, I bring to you a fast pardon and my lord's love and friendship. It repents him and is sorry that he ever has done, spoken or trespassed against you and therefor you shall have a good appointment and also amends. He shall give to you Bellin the ram and all his lineage from now forth on to doomsday in such wise that wheresomever you find them in field or in wood that you may freely bite and eat them without any forfeit. And also the

forwrought: ruined

king grants to you that you may hunt and do the worst you can to Reynard and all his lineage without misdoing. This fair great privilege will the king grant to you ever to hold of him and the king wills that you swear to him never to misdo, but do him homage and fealty. I counsel you to do this, for you may do it honorably."

Thus was the peace made by Firapeel the leopard friendly and well and that cost Bellin the ram his tabard [127] and also his life. And the wolf's lineage hold these privileges of the king and into this day they devour and eat Bellin's lineage where that they may find them. This debate was begun in an evil time, for the peace could never sith be made between them.

The king did forth with his court and feasted length twelve days longer for love of the bear and the wolf, so glad was he of the making of this peace.

XXIII. *How the King Held His Feast and How Lampreel* [128] *the Coney Complained Unto the King Upon Reynard the Fox*

To this great feast came all manner of beasts, for the king did do cry this feast over all in that land. There was the most joy and mirth that ever was seen among beasts. There was danced mannerly the hovedance with shawms, trumpets, and all manner of minstrelsy. The king did do ordain so much meat that everyone found enough and there was no beast in all his land so great nor so little but he was there and there were many fowls and birds also and all they that desired the king's friendship were there saving Reynard the fox, the red false pilgrim, which lay in a wait to do harm and thought it was not good for him to be there. Meat and drink flowed there. There were

tabard: mantle   *coney*: rabbit   *hovedance*: court dance
shawm: an oboe-like in-
  strument

107

plays and esbatements. The feast was full of melody. One might have lust to see such a feast.

And right as the feast had dured eight days, about midday came in the coney Lampreel tofore the king where he sat on the table with the queen and said all heavily that all they heard him that were there, "My lord, have pity on my complaint, which is of great force and murder that Reynard the fox would have done to me yestermorrow. As I came running by his burrow at Maleperduys, he stood before his door without like a pilgrim. I supposed to have passed by him peaceably toward this feast; and when he saw me come, he came against me saying his beads. I saluted him but he spoke not one word, but he raught out his right foot and dubbed me in the neck between my ears that I had weened I should have lost my head. But, God be thanked, I was so light that I sprang from him. With much pain came I of his claws. He grimmed as he had been angry because he held me no faster. Though I escaped from him, I lost my one ear and I had four great holes in my head of his sharp nails that the blood sprang out and that I was nigh all aswoon. But for the great fear of my life, I sprang and ran so fast from him that he could not overtake me. See, my lord, these great wounds that he has made to me with his sharp long nails. I pray you to have pity on me and that you will punish this false traitor and murderer or else shall there no man go and come over the heath in safety while he haunts his false and shrewd rule."

XXIV. *How Corbant* [129] *the Rook Complained on the Fox for the Death of His Wife*
Right as the coney had made an end of his complaint came in Corbant the rook flown in the place tofore the king and

esbatements: amuse-ments	*lust*: delight	*raught*: reached
	dubbed: struck	*haunts*: practices

said, "Dear lord, hear me! I bring you here a piteous complaint. I went today by the morrow with Sharpbeak,[130] my
wife, for to play upon the heath and there lay Reynard the
fox down on the ground like a dead caitiff. His eyes stared
and his tongue hung long out of his mouth like a hound had
been dead. We tasted and felt his belly, but we found thereon
no life. Tho went my wife and harkened and laid her ear
tofore his mouth for to wit if he drew his breath, which misfell her evil. For the false fell fox awaited well his time and
when he saw her so nigh him, he caught her by the head and
bit it off. Tho was I in great sorrow and cried loud, 'Alas!
Alas! What is there happed?' Then stood he hastily up and
raught so covetously after me that for fear of death I trembled
and flew upon a tree thereby and saw from far how the false
caitiff ate and slonked [131] her in so hungrily that he left neither
flesh nor bone, no more but a few feathers. The small feathers
he slang them in with the flesh. He was so hungry he would
well have eaten twain. Tho went he his street; tho flew
I down with great sorrow and gathered up the feathers for to
show them to you here. I would not be again in such peril and
fear as I was there for a thousand marks of the finest gold that
ever came out of Araby. My lord the king, see here this piteous
work! These be the feathers of Sharpbeak, my wife. My lord,
if you will have worship, you must do herefor justice and
avenge you in such wise as man may fear and hold of you. For
if you suffer thus your safe-conduct to be broken, you yourself shall not go peaceably in the highways. For those lords
that do not justice and suffer that the law be not executed upon
the thieves, murderers, and them that misdo, they be partners
tofore God of all their misdeeds and trespasses and everyone

misfell: mischanced   *slonked*: devoured

109

then will be a lord himself. Dear lord, see well tofore to keep yourself!"

xxv. *How the King Was Sore Angry of These Complaints*

Noble the king was sore moved and angry when he had heard these complaints of the coney and of the rook. He was so fearful to look on that his eyes glimmered as fire. He brayed as loud as a bull in such wise that all the court quaked for fear. At the last, he said crying, "By my crown and by the truth that I owe to my wife, I shall so awreak and avenge this trespass that it shall be long spoken of after that my safe-conduct and my commandment is thus broken. I was overnice that I believed so lightly the false shrew. His false flattering speech deceived me. He told me he would go to Rome and for thence oversea to the Holy Land. I gave him mail and palster and made of him a pilgrim and meant all truth. Oh what false touches can he! How can he stuff the sleeve with flocks! [132] But this caused my wife; it was all by her counsel. I am not the first that has been deceived by woman's counsel by which many a great hurt has befallen. I pray and command all them that hold of me and desire my friendship, be they here or whersomever they be, that they with their counsel and deeds help me to avenge this overgreat trespass that we and ours may abide in honor and worship and this false thief in shame that he no more trespass against our safeguard. I will myself in my person help thereto all that I may."

Isegrim the wolf and Bruin the bear heard well the king's words and hoped well to be avenged on Reynard the fox, but they dared not speak one word. The king was so sore moved that none dared well speak.

At last the queen spoke, "Sire pour dieu ne croyes mye toutes

awreak: requite   *overnice*: very foolish

choses que on vous dye et ne Iures pas legierment. A man of worship should not lightly believe nor swear greatly unto the time he knew the matter clearly and also he ought by right hear that other party speak. There be many that complain on other and be in the default themselves. Audi alteram partem; hear that other party! I have truly held the fox for good and upon that he meant no falsehood. I helped him that I might. But howsomever it comes or goes, is he evil or good, methinks for your worship that you should not proceed against him over-hastily. That were not good nor honest, for he may not escape from you. You may prison him or flee [133] him, he must obey your judgment."

Then said Firapeel the leopard, "My lord, methinks my lady here hath said to you truth and given you good counsel. Do you well and follow her and take advice of your wife's counsel; and if he be found guilty in the trespasses that now to you be showed, let him be sore punished according to his trespasses. And if he come not hither ere this feast be ended and excuse him as he ought of right to do, then do as the council shall advise you. But and if he were twice as much false and ill as he is, I would not counsel that he should be done to more than right."

Isegrim the wolf said, "Sir Firapeel, all we agree to the same as far as it pleases my lord the king. It cannot be better. But though Reynard were now here and he cleared him of double so many complaints, yet should I bring forth against him [134] that he had forfeited his life. But I will now be still and say not, because he is not present and yet above all this he has told the king of certain treasure lying in Krekenpit in Hulsterloo. There was never lied a greater lesing! Therewith he had us all beguiled and has sore hindered me and the bear. I dare lay my life thereon that he said not thereof a true word. Now robs he and steals upon the heath all that go forth by his house. Nevertheless, Sir Firapeel, what that pleases the king and you, that must well be done. But and if he would have come hither, he might have been here for he had knowledge by the king's messenger."

The king said, "We will no otherwise send for him, but I command all them that owe me service and will my honor and worship that they make them ready to the war at the end of six days, all of them that be archers and have bows, guns, bombards, horsemen and footmen, that all these be ready to besiege Maleperduys. I shall destroy Reynard the fox if I be a king! You lords and sirs, what say you hereto? Will you do this with a good will?"

And they said and cried all, "Yea, we, lord! When that you will, we shall all go with you!"

XXVI. *How Grimbert the Dasse Warned the Fox That the King Was Wroth with Him and Would Slay Him*

All these words heard Grimbert the dasse, which was his brotherson.[135] He was sorry and angry. If it might have profited, he ran then the highway to Maleperduysward. He spared neither bush nor haw,[136] but he hasted so sore that he sweat. He sorrowed in himself for Reynard, his red eme, and as he went he said to himself, "Alas, in what danger be you come in! Where shall you become? Shall I see you brought from life to death or else exiled out of the land? Truly, I may be well sorrowful, for you be head of our lineage. You be wise of counsel; you be ready to help your friends when they have need; you can so well show your reasons that where you speak you win all."

With such manner wailing and piteous words came Grim-

bombards: stone-throw-
  ing cannons

bert to Maleperduys. And found Reynard, his eme, there standing which had gotten two pigeons as they came first out of their nest to assay if they could fly; and because the feathers on their wings were too short they fell down to the ground. And as Reynard was gone out to seek his meat, he espied them and caught them and was come home with them.

And when he saw Grimbert coming, he tarried and said, "Welcome, my best beloved nephew that I know in all my kindred! You have run fast. You be all besweat. Have you any new tidings?"

"Alas," said he, "lief eme, it stands evil with you. You have lost both life and good. The king hath sworn that he shall give you a shameful death. He hath commanded all his folk within six days for to be here, archers, footmen, horsemen, and people in wains. And he has guns, bombards, tents, and pavillions. And also he has done loaded torches.[137] See tofore you! For you have need. Isegrim and Bruin be better now with the king than I am with you. All that they will is done. Isegrim has done him to understand that you be a thief and a murderer. He has great envy of you. Lampreel the coney and Corbant the rook have made a great complaint also. I sorrow much for your life that for dread I am all sick."

"Puff!" said the fox. "Dear nephew, is there nothing else? Be you so sore afraid hereof? Make good cheer! Hardly though the king himself and all that be in the court had sworn my death yet shall I be exalted above them all. They may all fast jangle, clatter, and give counsel; but the court may not prosper without me and my wiles and subtlety."

xxvii. *How Reynard the Fox Came Another Time to the Court*

"Dear nephew, let all these things pass and come herein and see what I shall give you, a good pair of fat pigeons. I love no meat better. They be good to digest. They may almost be swallowed in all whole. The bones be half blood; I eat them with that other. I feel myself otherwhile encumbered in my stomach; therefore eat I gladly light meat. My wife Ermelin shall receive us friendly, but tell her nothing of this thing, for she should take it overheavily. She is tender of heart. She might for fear fall in some sickness. A little thing goes sore to her heart. And tomorrow early I will go with you to the court. And if I may come to speech and may be heard, I shall so answer that I shall touch some nigh enough. Nephew, will you not stand by me as a friend ought to do to another?"

"Yes truly, dear eme," said Grimbert, "and all my good is at your commandment."

"God thank you, nephew," said the fox. "That is well said. If I may live, I shall quit it you."

"Eme," said Grimbert, "you may well come tofore all the lords and excuse you. There shall none arrest you nor hold as long as you be in your word.[138] The queen and the leopard have gotten that."

Then said the fox, "Therefore I am glad. Then I care not for the best of them a hair. I shall well save myself."

They spoke no more hereof, but went forth into the burrow and found Ermelin there sitting by her younglings, which arose up anon and received them friendly. Grimbert saluted his aunt and the children with friendly words. The two pigeons were made ready for their supper, which Reynard had taken. Each of them took his part as far as it would stretch. If each of them had had one more, there should but little have left over.

The fox said, "Lief nephew, how like you my children? Rossell and Reynardin,[139] they shall do worship to all our lineage. They begin already to do well. That one catches well

114

a chicken and that other a pullet. They con well also duck in the water after lapwinches and ducks. I would oft send them for provender, but I will first teach them how they shall keep them from the grins, from the hunters and from the hounds. If they were so far come that they were wise, I dared well trust to them that they should well victual us in many good diverse meats that we now lack. And they like and follow me well, for they play all grimming and where they hate they look friendly and merrily. For thereby they bring them under their feet and bite the throat asunder. This is the nature of the fox. They be swift in their takings, which pleases me well."

"Eme," said Grimbert, "you may be glad that you have such wise children and I am glad of them also because they be of my kin."

"Grimbert," said the fox, "you have sweat and be weary. It were high tide that you were at your rest."

"Eme, if it please you, it thinks me good." Tho lay they down on a litter made of straw; the fox, his wife, and his children went all to sleep. But the fox was all heavy and lay, sighed, and sorrowed how he might best excuse himself.

On the morrow early he roomed his castle and went with Grimbert. But he took leave first of Dame Ermelin his wife and of his children and said, "Think not long.[140] I must go to the court with Grimbert, my cousin. If I tarry somewhat, be not afraid; and if you hear any ill tidings, take it always for the best. And see well to yourself and keep our castle well. I shall do yonder the best I can, after that I see how it goes."

"Alas, Reynard," said she, "how have you now thus taken upon you for to go to court again? The last time that you were there, you were in great jeopardy of your life. And you said you would never come there more."

lapwinches: lapwings

"Dame," said the fox, "the adventure of the world is wonderly. It goes otherwhile by weening.[141] Many one weens to have a thing which he must forego. I must needs now go thither. Be content it is all without dread. I hope to come at all the longest within five days again."

Herewith he departed and went with Grimbert to the courtward. And when they were upon the heath, then said Reynard, "Nephew, sith I was last shriven I have done many shrewd turns. I would you would hear me now of all that I have trespassed in. I made the bear to have a great wound for the mail, which was cut out of his skin, and also I made the wolf and his wife to lose their shoes. I peased the king with great lesings and bore him on hand that the wolf and the bear would have betrayed him and would have slain him. I made the king right wroth with them where they deserved it not. Also I told to the king that there was great treasure in Hulster-loo, of which he was never the better nor richer, for I lied all that I said. I led Bellin the ram and Cuwart the hare with me and slew Cuwart and sent to the king by Bellin Cuwart's head in scorn and I dowed [142] the coney between his ears that I almost benam his life, for he escaped against my will. He was to me overswift. The rook may well complain, for I swallowed in Dame Sharpbeak his wife. And also I have forgotten one thing the last time that I was shriven to you, which I have sith bethought me and it was a great deceit that I did which I now will tell you.

"I came with the wolf walking between Houthulst and Elverding.[143] There saw we go a red mare and she had a black colt or a foal of four months old, which was good and fat. Isegrim was almost starved for hunger and prayed me go to the mare and wit of her if she would sell her foal.

wonderly: surprising   *turns*: wrongs   *peased*: appeased
dowed: nipped   *benam*: took

"I ran fast to the mare and asked that of her. She said she would sell it for money. I demanded of her how she would sell it. She said, 'It is written on my hinder foot. If you can read and be a clerk, you may come and read it.' Tho wist I well where she would be and I said, 'Nay, forsooth I cannot read and also I desire not to buy your child. Isegrim has sent me hither and would fain know the price thereof.' The mare said, 'Let him come then himself and I shall let him have knowledge.' I said 'I shall' and hastily went to Isegrim and said, 'Eme, will you eat your bellyfull of this colt, so go fast to the mare for she tarries after you. She has done written the price of her colt under her foot. She would that I should have read it, but I can not one letter, which me sore repents. For I went never to school. Eme, will you buy that colt, can you read so may you buy it.'

" 'Oi, nephew, that can I well! What should me let? I can well French, Latin, English, and Dutch. I have gone to school at Oxford. I have also with old and ancient doctors been in the audience and heard pleas and also have given sentence. I am licensed in both laws.[144] What manner writing that any man can devise, I can read it as perfectly as my name. I will go to her and shall anon understand the price.'

"And he bade me to tarry for him and he ran to the mare and asked her how she would sell her foal or keep it. She said, 'The sum of the money stands written after on my foot.' He said, 'Let me read it.' She said 'Do' and lifted up her foot, which was new shod with iron and six strong nails and she smote him without missing on his head that he fell down as he had been dead. A man should well have ridden a mile ere he arose. The mare trotted away with her colt and she left Isegrim lying shrewdly hurt and wounded. He lay and bled and howled as a hound.

THE HISTORY OF REYNARD THE FOX

"I went tho to him and said, 'Sir Isegrim, dear eme, how is it now with you? Have you eaten enough of the colt? Is your belly full? Why give you me no part? I did your errands. Have you slept your dinner? [145] I pray you tell me what was written under the mare's foot. What was it, prose or rhyme, meter or verse? I would fain know it. I trow it was cantum,[146] for I heard you sing methought from far, for you were so wise that no man could read it better than you.'

" 'Alas, Reynard, alas,' said the wolf, 'I pray you to leave your mocking. I am so foul arrayed and sore hurt that a heart of stone might have pity on me. The whore with her long leg had an iron foot. I weened the nails thereof had been lettered and she hit me at the first stroke six great wounds in my head that almost it is cloven. Such manner letters shall I never more desire to read.'

" 'Dear eme, is that the truth that you tell me? I have great marvel! I held you for one of the wisest clerks that now live. Now I hear well it is true that I long sith have read and heard that the best clerks be not the wisest men. The lay people otherwise wax wise. The cause that these clerks be not the wisest is that they study so much in the cunning and science that they therein dool.' [147] Thus brought I Isegrim in this great last and harm that he uneath beheld his life.

"Leif nephew, now have I told you all my sins that I remember. Whatsoever fall at the court, I wot never how it shall stand with me there. I am not now so sore afraid, for I am clear from sin. I will gladly come to mercy and receive penance by your counsel."

Grimbert said, "The trespasses be great. Nevertheless, who that is dead must abide dead and therefore I will forgive it you altogether with the fear that you shall suffer therefor ere you

dool: become dull

shall con excuse you of the death. And hereupon I will assoil you. But the most hinder [148] that you shall have shall be that you sent Cuwart's head to the court and that you blinded the king with subtle lies. Eme, that was right evil done."

The fox said, "What lief nephew! Who that will go through the world this to hear and that to see and that other to tell, truly it may not clearly be done. How should any man handle honey but if he licked his fingers. I am oftimes rored and pricked in my conscience as to love God above all things and my even Christian as myself as is to God well acceptable and according to his law. But how ween you that reason within forth fights against the outward will? Then stand I all still in myself that methinks I have lost all my wits and wot not what me ails, I am then in such a thought. I have now all left my sins and hate all thing that is not good and climb in high contemplation above his commandments. But this special grace have I when I am alone. But in a short while after when the world comes in me, then find I in my way so many stones and the footspoors that these loose prelates and rich priests go in that I am anon taken again. Then comes the world and will have this and the flesh will live pleasantly, which lays tofore me so many things that I then lose all my good thoughts and purpose. I hear there sing, pipe, laugh, play, and all mirth. And I hear that these prelates and rich curates preach and say all otherwise than they think and do. There learn I to lie the lesings been most used in the lords' courts. Certainly lords, ladies, priests, and clerks make most lesings. Men dare not tell to the lords now the truth. There is default. I must flatter and lie also, or else I should be shut without the door. I have oft heard men say truth and rightfully and have their reason made with the lesing like to their purpose and brought it in and went through

even: fellow

119

because their matters should seem the fairer. The lesing oftimes comes unavised and falls in the matter unwittingly and so when she is well clad it goes forth through with that other.

"Dear nephew, thus must men now lie here and there, say sooth, flatter and menace, pray and curse, and seek every man upon his feeblest and weakest. Who otherwise will now haunt and use the world than devise a lesing in the fairest wise and that bewimple with kerchiefs about in such wise that men take it for a truth? He is not run away from his master [149] can he that subtlety in such wise that he stammer not in his words and may then be heard. Nephew, this man may do wonder. He may wear scarlet and grise. He wins in the spiritual law and temporal also and wheresomever he has to do. Now be there many false shrews that have great envy that they [150] have so great fordeal and ween that they can also well lie and take on them to lie and to tell it forth. He would fain eat of the fat morsels, but he is not believed nor heard. And many be there that be so plump and foolish that when they ween best to pronounce and show their matter and conclude, they fall beside and out thereof and cannot then help themselves and leave their matter without tail or head and he is accounted for a fool. And many mock them therewith. But who can give to his lesings a conclusion and pronounce it without tattling like as it were written tofore him and that he can so blind the people that his lesing shall better be believed than the truth, that is the man! What cunning is it to say the truth, that is good to do? How laugh these false subtle shrews that give counsel to make these lesings and set them forth and make unright go about right and make bills and set in things that never were thought nor said and teach men see through their fingers [151] and all for to win money and let their tongues to hire for to maintain and

bewimple: envelop   *grise*: costly grey fur   *fordeal*: advantage
tattling: faltering

strengthen their lesings! Alas, nephew, this is an evil cunning, of which life, scathe, and hurt may come thereof.

"I say not but that otherwhile men must jape, bourd, and lie in small things. For whoso says always truth, he may not now go nowhere through the world. There be many that play Placebo.¹⁵² Whoso always says the truth shall find many lettings in his way. Men may well lie when it is need and after amend it by counsel.¹⁵³ For all trespasses there is mercy. There is no man so wise but he dools otherwhile."

Grimbert said, "Well, dear eme, what things shall you let? You know all thing at the narrowest. You should bring me hastily in doting. Your reasons pass my understanding. What need have you to shrive you? You should yourself by right be the priest and let me and other sheep come to you for to be shriven. You know the state of the world in such wise as no man may halt tofore you." ¹⁵⁴

With such manner talking they came walking into the court. The fox sorrowed somewhat in his heart. Nevertheless, he bore it out and struck forth through all the folk till he came into the place where the king himself was.

And Grimbert was always by the fox and said, "Eme, be not afraid and make good cheer. Who that is hardy, the adventure helps him. Oftimes one day is better than sometimes a whole year."

The fox said, "Nephew, you say truth. God thank you! You comfort me well."

And forth he went and looked grimly here and there as who says, "What will you? Here come I!" He saw there many of his kin standing which yonned him but little good, as the otter, beaver, and others to the number of ten whom I shall name afterwards. And some were there that loved him. The fox

otherwhile: sometimes	*letting*: hindrances	*dools*: errs
let: hinder	*adventure*: fortune	*yonned*: wished

came in and fell down on his knees tofore the king and began his words and said:

XXVIII. *How Reynard the Fox Excused Him Before the King*

"God, from whom nothing may be hidden and above all things is mighty, save my lord the king and my lady the queen and give them grace to know who has right and who has wrong! For there live many in the world that seem otherwise outward than they be within. I would that God showed openly every man's misdeeds and all their trespasses stood written in their foreheads; and it cost me more than I now say, and that you, my lord the king, knew as much as I do how I disposed me both early and late in your service. And therefore am I complained on of the evil shrews, and with lesings, and put out of your grace and conceit, and would charge me [155] with great offences without deserving against all right. Wherefore I cry out harrow [156] on them that so falsely have belied me and brought me in such trouble. How be it, I hope and know you both, my lord and lady, for so wise and discreet that you be not led nor believe such lesings nor false tales out of the right way, for you have not been woned so to do. Therefore, dear lord, I beseech you to consider by your wisdom all thing by right and law, is it in deed or in speech. Do every man right. I desire no better. He that is guilty and found faulty, let him be punished. Men shall well know ere I depart out of this court who that I am. I cannot flatter. I will always show openly my head."

How the King Answered Upon Reynard's Excuse

All they that were in the palace were all still and wondered that the fox spoke so stoutly.

disposed: conducted   *conceit*: esteem   *woned*: accustomed

The king said, "Ha, Reynard, how well can you your fallacy and salutation do! But your fair words may not help you. I think well that you shall this day for your works be hanged by your neck. I will not much chide with you, but I shall shorten your pain. That you love us well, that have you well shown on the coney and on Corbant the rook. Your falseness and your false inventions shall without long tarrying make you to die. A pot may go so long to water that at the last it comes tobroken home. I think your pot, that so oft has deceived us, shall now hastily be broken."

Reynard was in great fear of these words. He would well he had been at Cologne when he came thither. Then thought he I must here through how that I do.[157]

"My lord the king," said he, "it were well reasoned that you heard my words all out. Tho I were damned to the death, yet ought you to hear my words out. I have yet heretofore time given to you many a good counsel and profitable and in need always have bided by you where other beasts have wiked and gone their way. If now the evil beasts with false matters have tofore you with wrong belied me and I might not come to my excuse, ought I not then to plain? I have tofore this seen that I should be heard before another. Yet might these things well change and come in their old state. Old good deeds ought to be remembered. I see here many of my lineage and friends standing that seem they set now little by me, which nevertheless should sore dere in their hearts that you, my lord the king, should destroy me wrongfully. If you so did, he should destroy the truest servant that you have in all your lands. What ween you, sir king, had I known myself guilty in any feat or broke, that I would have come hither to the law among all my ene-

tobroken: broken to pieces	*wiked*: withdrawn *dere*: grieve	*plain*: complain *broke*: offense

mies? Nay, sir, nay, not for all the world of red gold! For I was free and at large. What need had I to do that? But, God be thanked, I know myself clear of all misdeeds that I dare well come openly in the light and to answer to all the complaints that any man can say on me. But when Grimbert brought me first these tidings, tho was I not well pleased, but half from myself [158] that I lept here and there as an unwise man. And had I not been in the censures of the church, I had without tarrying have come; but I went doling [159] on the heath and wist not what to do for sorrow.

"And then it happened that Martin,[160] my eme, the ape, met with me, which is wiser in clergy than some priest. He has been advocate for the Bishop of Camerik [161] nine years during. He saw me in this great sorrow and heaviness and said to me 'Dear cousin, methinks you are not well with yourself. What ails you? Who has displeased you? Things that touch charge [162] ought to be given in knowledge to friends. A true friend is a great help. He finds oft better counsel than he that the charge rests on. For whosomever is charged with matters is so heavy and accumbered with them that oft he cannot begin to find the remedy, for such be so woelike as they had lost their inwit.'

"I said, 'Dear eme, you say the truth, for in like wise is fallen to me. I am brought into a great heaviness undeserved and not guilty by one to whom I have always been a hearty and great friend; that is the coney which came to me yesterday in the morning whereas I sat before my house and said matins. He told me he would go to the court and saluted me friendly and I him again. Tho said he to me "Good Reynard, I am ahungered and am weary. Have you any meat?" I said "Yea, enough, come near." Tho gave I him a couple of manchets

clergy: learning   *charge*: burden   *inwit*: understanding
manchets: loaves of fine
  white bread

124

with sweet butter. It was upon a Wednesday, on which day I am not wont to eat any flesh. And also I fasted because of this feast of Whitsuntide which approached; for who that will taste of the overest wisehood and live ghostly in keeping the commandments of our Lord, he must fast and make him ready against the high feasts. Et vos estote parati,[163] dear eme. I gave him fair white bread with sweet butter wherewith a man might well be eased that were much hungry.

" 'And when he had eaten his bellyfull, tho came Rossel, my youngest son, and would have taken away that was left. For young children would always fain eat and with that he tasted for to have taken somewhat. The coney smote Rossel tofore his mouth that the teeth bled and fell down half aswoon. When Reynardin, my eldest son, saw that, he sprang to the coney and caught him by the head and should have slain him had I not rescued him. I helped him that he went from him [164] and beat my child sore therefore.

" 'Lampreel the coney ran to my lord the king and said I would have murdered him. See, eme, thus come I in the word and I am not laid in the blame.[165] And yet he complains and I complain not.

" 'After this came Corbant the rook flying with a sorrowful noise. I asked what him ailed and he said "Alas, my wife is dead. Yonder lies a dead hare full of mathes and worms and there she ate so much thereof that the worms have bitten atwo her throat." I asked him how came that by. He would not speak a word more, but flew his way and let me stand. Now says he that I have bitten and slain her. How should I come so nigh her, for she flies and I go afoot. Behold, dear eme, thus am I borne on hand.[166] I may say well that I am unhappy, but

overest: supreme   *ghostly*: holily   *tasted*: reached
mathes: maggots

125

peradventure it is for my old sins. It were good for me if I could patiently suffer it.'

"The ape said to me, 'Nephew, you shall go to court tofore the lords and excuse you.' 'Alas, eme, that may not be. For the archdeacon has put me in the Pope's curse because I counselled Isegrim the wolf for to leave his religion at Elmare and forsake his habit. He complained to me that he lived so straitly as in long fasting and many things reading and singing that he could not endure it. I had pity of his complaining and I helped him as a true friend that he came out, which now me sore repents. For he labors all that he can against me to the king for to do me be hanged. Thus does he evil for good. See, eme, thus am I at the end of all my wits and of counsel. For I must go to Rome for an absolution and then shall my wife and children suffer much harm and blame. For these evil beasts that hate me shall do to them all the hurt they may and fordrive them where they can. And I would well defend them if I were free of the curse, for then would I go to the court and excuse me where now I dare not. I should do great things if I came among the great people. I am afraid God should plague me.'

" 'Nay, cousin, be not afraid. Ere I should suffer you in this sorrow, I know the way to Rome well. I understand me on this work. I am called there Martin, the bishop's clerk, and am well beknown there. I shall do cite the archdeacon and take a plea against him and shall bring with me for you an absolution against his will. For I know there all that is for to be done or left. There dwells Simon, my eme,[167] which is great and mighty there. Who that may give ought, he helps him anon. There is Prentout,[168] Waitscathe,[169] and other of my friends and allies. Also I shall take some money with me if I need any. The

fordrive: persecute   *cite*: summon to court

prayer is with gifts hardy.[170] With money always the right goes forth. A true friend shall for his friend adventure both life and good and so shall I for you in your right.

" 'Cousin, make good cheer! I shall not rest after tomorrow till I come to Rome and I shall solicit your matters. And go you to the court as soon as you may. All your misdeeds and those sins that have brought you in the great sentence and curse, I make you quit of them and take them in myself. When you come to the court, you shall find there Rukenaw [171] my wife, her two sisters, and my three children and many more of our lineage. Dear cousin, speak to them hardily. My wife is sonderly wise and will gladly do somewhat for her friends. Who that has need of help shall find on her great friendship. One shall always seek on his friends tho he have angered them. For blood must creep where it cannot go.[172] And if so be that you be so overcharged that you may have no right, then send to me by night and day to the court of Rome and let me have knowledge thereof. And all those that be in the land, is it king or queen, wife or man, I shall bring them all in the Pope's curse and send there an interdict that no man shall read nor sing nor christen children nor bury the dead nor receive sacraments till that you shall have good right. Cousin, this shall I well get for the Pope is so sore old that he is but little set by and the cardinal of pure gold has all the might of the court. He is young and great of friends. He has a concubine whom he much loves; and what she desires, that gets she anon. See, cousin, she is my niece and I am great and may do much with her in such wise what I desire I fail not of it, but am always furthered therein. Wherefore, cousin, bid my lord the king that he do you right. I wot well he will not warn you, for the right is heavy enough to every man.'

sonderly: especially   *overcharged*: accused excessively

"My lord the king, when I heard this I laughed and with great gladness came hither and have told you all truth. If there be any in this court that can lay on me any other matter with good witness and prove it as ought to be to a noble man, let me then make amends according to the law; and if he will not leave off hereby then set me a day and field and I shall make good on him all so far as he be of as good birth as I am and to me like; and who that can with fighting get the worship of the field, let him have it. This right has stood yet hitherto and I will not it should be broken by me. The law and right do no man wrong."

All the beasts, both poor and rich, were all still when the fox spoke so stoutly. The coney Lampreel and the rook were so sore afraid that they durst not speak, but piked and striked them out of the court both two. And when they were in a room far in the plain, they said, "God grant that this fell murderer may fare evil! He can bewrap and cover his false-hood that his words seem as true as the gospel. Hereof knows no man than we. How should we bring witness? It is better that we wike and depart than we should hold a field and fight with him. He is so shrewd, yea, though there of us were five, we could not defend us but that he should slay us all."

Isegrim the wolf and Bruin the bear were woe in themselves when they saw these twain room the court.

The king said, "If any man will complain, let him come forth and we shall hear him. Yesterday came here so many. Where be they now Reynard is here?"

The fox said, "My lord, there be many that complain that and if they saw their adversary they would be still and make no plaint. Witness now of Lampreel the coney and Corbant the rook, which have complained on me to you in my absence,

piked: made off   *striked*: hastened   *room*: area but now that I am come in your presence they flee away and dare not abide by their words. If men should believe false shrews, it should do much harm and hurt to the good men; as for me, it skills not.[173] Nevertheless, my lord, if they had by your commandment asked of me forgiveness, how be it they have greatly trespassed, yet I had for your sake pardoned and forgiven them. For I will not be out of charity nor hate nor complain on my enemies, but I set all thing in God's hands. He shall work and avenge it as it pleases Him."

The king said, "Reynard, methinks you be grieved. As you say, are you withinforth as you seem outward? Nay, it is not so clear nor so open nowhere nigh as you here have shown. I must say what my grief is which touches your worship and life, that is to wit, that you have done a foul and shameful trespass when I had pardoned you all your offences and trespasses and you promised to go over the sea on pilgrimage and gave to you mail and staff. And after this you sent me by Bellin the ram the mail again and therein Cuwart's head. How might you do a more reprovable trespass! How were you so hardy to dare to me do such a shame? Is it not evil done to send to a lord his servant's head? You cannot say nay hereagainst, for Bellin the ram, which was our chaplain, told us all the matter how it happed. Such reward as he had when he brought us the message, the same shall you have or right shall fail!"

Tho was Reynard so sore afraid that he wist not what to say. He was at his wit's end and looked about him piteously and saw many of his kin and allies that heard all this, but nought they said. He was all pale in his visage, but no man proffered him hand nor foot to help him.

The king said, "Thou subtle fellow and false shrew, why speak you not? Now dumb?"

The fox stood in great dread and sighed sore that all heard him. But the wolf and the bear were glad thereof.

XXIX. *How Dame Rukenaw Answered for the Fox to the King*

Dame Rukenaw the she-ape, Reynard's aunt, was not well pleased. She was great with the queen and well beloved. It happed well for the fox that she was there. For she understood all wisdom and she dared well speak whereas it to do was. Wherever she came, everyone was glad of her.

She said, "My lord the king, you ought not to be angry when you sit in judgment for that becomes not your noblesse. A man that sits in judgment ought to put from him all wrath and anger. A lord ought to have discretion that should sit in justice. I know better the points of the law than some that wear furred gowns. For I have learned many of them and was made cunning in the law. I had in the Pope's palace of Woerden [174] a good bed of hay, where other beasts lay on the hard ground. And also when I had there to do, I was suffered to speak and was heard tofore another because I knew so well the law. Seneca writes that a lord shall over all do right and law. He shall charge none to whom he has given his safeguard to above the right and law. The law ought not to hold [175] for no man. And every man that stands here would well bethink him what he has done and bedriven in his days. He should the better have patience and pity on Reynard. Let every man know himself. That is my counsel. There is none that stands so surely but otherwhile he falls or slides. Who that never misdid nor sinned is holy and good and has no need to amend him. When a man does amiss and then by counsel amends it, that is humanly and so ought he to do. But always to misdo and trespass and not to amend him, that is evil and a devilly life. Mark then what is written in the gospel. Estote misericordes,[176] be you merciful. Yet stands there more, Nolite iudicare et non iudicabi-mini,[177] deem you no man and you shall not be deemed. There stands also how the Pharisees brought a woman taken in avow-try and would have stoned her to death. They asked our Lord what he said thereto. He said, 'Who of you all is without sin let him cast the first stone.' Tho abode no man but left her there standing.

"Methinks it is so here. There be many that see a straw in another's eye that cannot see a balk in his own.[178] There be many that deem other and himself is worst of all. Though one fall oft and at last arises up and comes to mercy, he is not thereof damned. God receives all them that desire his mercy. Let no man condemn another, though they wist that he had done amiss. Yet let them see their own faults and then may they themselves correct first. And then Reynard, my cousin, should not fare the worst, for his father and grandfather have always been in more love and reputation in this court than Isegrim the wolf and Bruin the bear with all their friends and lineage. It has been heretofore an unlike comparison: the wis-dom of Reynard my cousin and the honor and worship of him that he has done [179] and the counsel of them, for they know not how the world goes. Methinks this court is all turned up so down. These false shrews, flatterers, and deceivers arise and wax great by the lords and be enhanced up and the good, true, and wise be put down. For they have been woned to counsel truly and for the honor of the king. I cannot see how this may stand long!"

Then said the king, "Dame, if he had done to you such tres-pass as he has done to other, it should repent you. Is it wonder that I hate him? He breaks always my safeguard. Have you not heard the complaints that here have been shown of him,

avowtry: adultery

of murder, of theft, and of treason? Have you such trust in him? Think you that he is thus good and clear, then set him upon the altar and worship and pray to him as a saint. But there is none in all the world that can say any good of him. You may say much for him, but in the end you shall find him all nought. He has neither kin nor wine nor friend that will enterprise to help him. He has so deserved. I have great marvel of you. I heard never of none that has fellowshipped with him that ever thanked him or said any good of him save you now, but always he has struck them with his tail."

The she-ape answered and said, "My lord, I love him and have him in great charity. And also I know a great deed that he once in your presence did whereof you could him great thank. Though now it be thus turned, yet shall the heaviest weigh most. A man shall love his friend by measure and not his enemy hate overmuch. Steadfastness and constance is fitting and behooves to the lords, howsomever the world turns. Me [180] ought not to praise too much the day till even be come. Good counsel is good for him that will do thereafter."

xxx. *A Parable* [181] *of a Man That Delivered a Serpent from Peril of Death*

"Now two years past came a man and a serpent here into this court for to have judgment which was to you and yours right doubtful. The serpent stood in a hedge whereas he supposed to have gone through, but he was caught in a snare by the neck that he might not escape without help but should have lost his life there. The man came forth by and the serpent called to him and cried and prayed the man that he would help him out of the snare or else he must there die.

"The man had pity of him and said 'If you promise to me

wine: friend   *enterprise*: attempt

that you will not envenom me nor do me no harm nor hurt, I shall help you out of this peril.' The serpent was ready and swore a great oath that he now nor never should do him harm nor hurt. Then he unloosened him and delivered him out of the snare and went forth together a good while that the serpent had great hunger, for he had not eaten a great while tofore and started to the man and would have slain him.

"The man started away and was afraid and said 'Will you now slay me? Have you forgotten the oath that you made to me that you should not misdo nor hurt me?'

"The serpent answered, 'I may do it good tofore all the world that I do.[182] The need of hunger may cause a man to break his oath.'

"The man said, 'If it may not be better, give me so long respite till we meet and find that may judge the matter by right.' The serpent granted thereto. Thus they went together so long that they found Tiselin the raven and Slindpere,[183] his son. There they rehearsed their reasons. Tiselin the raven judged anon that he should eat the man. He would fain have eaten his part and his son also.

"The serpent said to the man, 'How is it now? What think you? Have I not won?'

"The man said, 'How should a robber judge this? He should have availed thereby and also he is alone. There must be two or three at the least together; and that they understand the right and law and that they do, let the sentence go.[184] I am nevertheless ill on enough.' [185] They agreed and went forth together so long that they found the bear and the wolf, to whom they told their matter. And they anon judged that the serpent should slay the man, for the need of hunger breaks oath always. The man then was in great doubt and fear and the serpent came and cast his venom at him, but the man lept away from his with great pain and said, 'You do great wrong! That you thus lie in await to slay me, you have no right thereto!'

"The serpent said, 'Is it not enough yet? It has been twice judged.'

Chanticleer came forth and smote piteously his hands and his feathers and on each side of the bier went two sorrowful hens

" 'Yea,' said the man, 'that is of them that be wont to murder and rob. All that ever they swear and promise, they hold not. But I appeal this matter into the court tofore our lord and king and that you may not forsake. And what judgment that shall be given there, I shall obey and suffer and never to the contrary.'

"The bear and the wolf said that it should be so and that the serpent desired no better. They supposed if it should come tofore you, it should go there as they would. I trow you be well remembered hereof. Tho came they all to the court tofore you and the wolf's two children came with their father, which we call Emptybelly and Neverfull,[186] because they would eat of the man, for they howled for great hunger, wherefore you commanded them to avoid your court.

"The man stood in great dread and called upon your good grace and told how the serpent would have taken his life from him to whom he had saved his life and that above his open promise, he would have devoured him.

"The serpent answered, 'I have not trespassed and that I report me wholly unto the king, for I did it to save my life. For need of life one may break his oath and promise.' My lord, that time were you and your council herewith accumbered, for your noble grace saw the great sorrow of the man. And you would not that a man should for his gentleness and kindness be judged to death. And on the other sith, hunger and need to save the life seeks narrowly to be helped. Here was none in all the court that could nor knew the right hereof. There were some that would fain the man had been helped. I see them here standing. I wot well they said that they could not end this matter.

"Then commanded you that Reynard, my nephew, should come and say his advice in this matter. That time was he above all other believed and heard in the court. And you bade him give sentence according to the best right and we all shall follow him, for he knew the ground of the law.

sith: hand

135

"Reynard said, 'My lord, it is not possible to give a true sentence after their words, for in their saying be oft lesings. But and if I might see the serpent in the same peril and need that he was in when the man loosened him and unbound, then wist I well what I should say. And who that would do otherwise, he should misdo against right.'

"Then said you, 'My lord Reynard, that is well said. We all accord hereto, for no man can say better.' Then went the man and the serpent into the place whereas he found the serpent. Reynard bade that the serpent should be set in the snare in like wise as he was. And it was done.

"Then said you, 'My lord Reynard, how think you now? What judgment shall we give?'

"Then said Reynard the fox, 'My lord, now be they both like as they were tofore. They have neither won nor lost. See, my lord, how I judge for a right also far as it shall please your noble grace. If the man will now loosen and unbind the serpent upon the promise and oath that he tofore made to him, he may well do it. But if he think that he for any thing should be encumbered or hindered by the serpent or for need of hunger would break his oath and promise, then judge I that the man may go freely where he will and let the serpent abide still bound like as he might have done at the beginning, for he would have broken his oath and promise, whereas he helped him out of such fearful peril. Thus thinks me a rightful judgment that the man shall have his free choice like as he tofore had.'

"Lo, my lord, this judgment thought you good and all your council, which at that time were by you and followed the same, and praised Reynard's wisdom, that he had made the man quit and free. Thus the fox wisely kept your noble honor and worship as a true servant is bound to do to his lord. Where has the bear or the wolf done ever to you so much worship? They can well howl and blasen,[187] steal and rob, and eat fat morsels and fill their bellies. And then judge they for right and law that small thieves that steal hens and chickens should be hanged! But they themselves that steal kine, oxen, and horses, they shall go quit and be lords and seem as though they were wiser than Solomon, Avicenna,[188] or Aristotle. And each will be held high, proud, and prized of great deeds and hardy. But and they come whereas it is to do, they be the first that flee. Then must the simple go forth tofore and they keep the rearward behind. Och, my lord, these and other like to them be not wise, but they destroy town, castle, land, and people. They retch not whose house burns so that they may warm them by the coals. They seek all their own avail and singular profit. But Reynard the fox and all his friends and lineage sorrow and think to prefer the honor, worship, fordeal, and profit of their lord and for wise counsel, which oft more profits here than pride and boast. This does Reynard though he have no thanks. At the long [189] it shall be well known who is best and does most profit.

"My lord, you say that his kin and lineage draw all afterward from him and stand not by him for his falsehood and deceivable and subtle touches. I would another had said that! There should then such wrake be taken thereof that him might growl [190] that ever he saw him. But, my lord, we will forbear you.[191] You may say your pleasure and also I say it not by you. Were there any that would bedrive anything against you with words or with work, him would we so do to that men would say we had been there. There as fighting is, we be not woned to be afraid. My lord, by your leave I may well give you knowledge of Reynard's friends and kin. There be many of

wrake: revenge   *bedrive*: plot

137

them that for his sake and love will adventure life and good. I know myself for one. I am a wife. I should, if he had need, set my life and good for him. Also I have three full-waxen children, which be hardy and strong, whom I would altogether adventure for his love rather than I should see him destroyed. Yet had I liefer die than I saw them miscarry tofore my eyes, so well I love him.[192]

xxxi. Which Be Friends and Kin Unto Reynard the Fox

"The first child is named Bitelouse,[193] which is most cherished and can make much sport and game, wherefore is given to him the fat trencher and much other good meat, which comes well to profit of Fullrump,[194] his brother. And also my third child is a daughter and is named Hatenette.[195] She can well pick out lice and nits out of men's heads. These three be to each other true, wherefore I love them well."

Dame Rukenaw called them forth and said, "Welcome, my dear children, to me forth and stand by Reynard, your dear nephew." [196]

Then said she, "Come forth all you that be of my kin and Reynard's and let us pray the king that he will do to Reynard right of the land."

Tho came forth many a beast anon as, the squirrel, the mousehound,[197] the fitchews, the marten, the beaver with his wife Ordegele,[198] the genet, the ostrole,[199] the boussing and the ferret (these twain eat as fain poultry as does Reynard), the otter and Pantecroet [200] his wife, whom I had almost forgotten, yet were they tofore with the beaver enemies to the fox. But they dared not gainsay Dame Rukenaw, for they were afraid of her. She was also the wisest of all his kin of counsel and was most

genet: civet cat   boussing: polecat

doubted. There came also more than twenty other because of her for to stand by Reynard. There came also Dame Atrote [201] with her two sisters, the weasel and hermel, the ass, the back, the water rat, and many more to the number of forty which all came and stood by Reynard the fox.

"My lord the king," said Rukenaw, "come and see here if Reynard have any friends. Here may you see! We be your true subjects, which for you would adventure both life and good if you had need. Though you be hardy, mighty, and strong, our well-willed friendship cannot hurt you. Let Reynard the fox well bethink him upon these matters that you have laid against him; and if he cannot excuse them, then do him right. We desire no better. And this by right ought to no man be warned."

The queen then spoke, "This said I to him yesterday! But he was so fierce and angry that he would not hear it."

The leopard said also, "Sire, you may judge no further than your men give their verdict, for if you would go forth by will and might that were not worshipful for your estate. Hear always both parties and then by the best and wisest counsel give judgment discreetly according to the best right."

The king said, "This is all true, but I was so sore moved when I was informed of Cuwart's death and saw his head that I was hot and hasty. I shall hear the fox. Can he answer and excuse him of that is laid against him, I shall gladly let him go quit and also at the request of his good friends and kin."

Reynard was glad of these words and thought 'God thank my aunt! She has the rise do blossom again.[202] She has well helped me forth now. I have now a good foot to dance on. I shall now look out of my eyes [203] and bring forth the fairest

doubted: feared   *hermel*: ermine   *back*: bat
warned: denied

139

lesings that ever man heard and bring myself out of this danger.'

XXXII. *How the Fox with Subtlety Excused Him for the Death of Cuwart the Hare and of All Other Matters That Were Laid Against Him and How with Flattering Got Again His Peace of the King*

Then spoke Reynard the fox and said, "Alas, what say you? Is Cuwart dead? And where is Bellin the ram? What brought he to you when he came again? For I delivered to him three jewels. I would fain know where they be become. That one of them should he have given to you, my lord the king, and the other two to my lady the queen."

The king said, "Bellin brought us nought else but Cuwart's head like as I said tofore, whereof I took on him wrake. I made him to lose his life, for the foul caitiff said to me that he himself was of the counsel of the letters' making that were in the mail."

"Alas, my lord, is this very truth? Woe to me, caitiff, that ever I was born sith that these good jewels be thus lost. My heart will break for sorrow. I am sorry that I now live. What shall my wife say when she hears hereof? She shall go out of her wits for sorrow. I shall never also long as I live have her friendship. She shall make much sorrow when she hears therof."

The she-ape said, "Reynard, dear nephew, what profits that you make all this sorrow? Let it pass and tell us what these jewels were. Peradventure we shall find counsel to have them again if they be above earth. Master Akerin [204] shall labor for them in his books and also we shall curse for them in all churches [205] unto the time that we have knowledge where they be. They may not be lost."

"Nay, aunt, think not that, for they that have them will not likely depart from them. There was never king that ever gave so rich jewels as these be. Nevertheless, you have somewhat with your words eased my heart and made it lighter than it was. Alas, lo here you may see how he or they to whom a man trusts most is oft by him or them deceived. Tho I should go all the world through and my life in adventure set therefor, I shall wit where these jewels be become."

With a dissimulated and sorrowful speech said the fox, "Harken, ye all my kin and friends, I shall name to you these jewels, what they were, and then may you say that I have a great loss. That one of them was a ring of fine gold and within the ring next the finger were written letters enameled with sable and azure and there were three Hebrews' names therein. I could not myself read nor spell them, for I understood not that language. But Master Abrion of Trier,[206] he is a wise man. He understands well all manner of languages and the virtue of all manner herbs and there is no beast so fierce nor strong but he can dompt him. For if he see him once, he shall do as he will. And yet he believes not on God. He is a Jew, the wisest in cunning; and specially he knows the virtue of stones. I showed him once this ring. He said that they were those three names that Seth brought out of Paradise when he brought to his father Adam the oil of mercy. And whosoever bears on him these three names, he shall never be hurt by thunder nor lightning, nor no witchcraft shall have power over him, nor be tempted to do sin. And also he shall never take harm by cold though he lay three winter's long nights in the field, though it snowed, stormed, or froze never so sore, so great might have these words. Witness of Master Abrion! Without-forth on the ring stood a stone of three manner colors. The one

dompt: tame   *withoutforth*: on the
                        outside

141

part was like red crystal and shone like as fire had been therein in such wise that if anyone would go by night him behooved no other light, for the shining of the stone made and gave as great a light as it had been midday. That other part of the stone was white and clear as it had been burnished. Whoso had in his eyes any smart or soreness or in his body any swelling or headache or any sickness withoutforth, if he struck the stone on the place where the grief is, he shall anon be whole. Or if any man be sick in his body of venom or ill meat in his stomach, of colic, strangullion,[207] stone, fistula, or canker or any other sickness, save only the very death, let him lay this stone in a little water and let him drink it and he shall forthwith be whole and all quit of his sickness.

"Alas," said the fox, "we have good cause to be sorry to lose such a jewel. Furthermore, the third color was green like glass. But there were some sprinkles therein like purple. The master told for truth that who that bore this stone upon him should never be hurt of his enemy and that no man, were he ever so strong and hardy, that might misdo him. And wherever that he fought, he should have victory, were it by night or by day, all so far as he beheld it fasting. And also thereto wheresomever he went and in what fellowship, he should be beloved though they had hated him tofore. If he had the ring upon him, they should forget their anger as soon as they saw him. Also though he were all naked in a field against a hundred armed men, he should be well hearted and escape from them with worship. But he must be a noble gentle man and have no churl's conditions, for then the stone had no might. And because this stone was so precious and good, I thought in myself that I was not able nor worthy to bear it. And therefore I sent it to my dear lord for I know him for the most noble that now lives. And also all our welfare and worship lies on him and for he should be kept from all dread, need, and ungeluck.

"I found this ring in my father's treasure and in the same place I took a glass or a mirror and a comb which my wife would algates have. A man might wonder that saw these jewels. I sent these to my lady the queen, for I have found her good and gracious to me. This comb may not be too much prized. It was made of the bone of a clean noble beast named Panthera,[208] which feeds him between the great India and earthly paradise. He is so lusty fair and of color that there is no color under the heavens but some likeness is in him. Thereto he smells so sweet that the savor of him boots all sickness and for his beauty and sweet smelling all other beasts follow him, for by his sweet savor they be healed of all sicknesses. This panther has a fair bone, broad and thin. Whenso is that this beast is slain, all the sweet odor rests in the bone, which cannot be broken nor shall never rot nor be destroyed by fire, by water, nor by smiting. It is so hardy, tight, and fast and yet it is light of weight. The sweet odor of it has great might that who that smells it sets nought by no other lust in the world and is eased and quit of all manner diseases and infirmities. And also he is jocund and glad in his heart. This comb is polished as it were fine silver and the teeth of it be small and straight and between the greater teeth and the smaller is a large field and space where is carved many an image subtlely made and enamelled about with fine gold. The field is checked with sable and silver, enamelled with cybore [209] and azure. And therein is the history how Venus, Juno, and Pallas strove for the apple of gold which each of them would have had, which controversy was set upon Paris that he should give it to the fairest of them three.

ungeluck: misfortune   *algates*: notwithstanding   *boots*: cures

143

"Paris was that time a herdsman and he kept his father's beasts and sheep without Troy. When he had received the apple, Juno promised to him if he would judge that she might have the apple, he should have the most richness of the world. Pallas said if she might have the apple she would give him wisdom and strength and make him so great a lord that he should overcome all his enemies and whom he would. Venus said 'What need you richness or strength? Are you not Priamus's son and Hector is your brother, which have all Asia under their power? Are not you one of the possessors of great Troy? If you will give to me the apple, I shall give you the richest treasure of the world and that shall be the fairest woman that ever had life on earth, nor never shall none be born fairer than she. Then shall you be richer than rich and shall climb above all other, for that is the treasure that no man can praise enough. For honest, fair, and good women can put away many a sorrow from the heart. They be shamefast and wise and bring a man in very joy and bliss.'

"Paris heard this Venus, which presented him this great joy and fair lady, and prayed her to name this fair lady that was so fair and where she was. Venus said, 'It is Helen, King Menelaus's wife of Greece. There lives not a nobler, richer, gentler, nor wiser wife in all the world.' Then Paris gave to her the apple and said that she was fairest. How that he got afterwards Helen by the help of Venus and how he brought her into Troy and wedded her, the great love and jolly life that they had together, was all carved in the field, everything by himself [210] and the story written.

"Now you shall hear of the mirror. The glass that stood thereon was of such virtue that men might see therein all that was done within a mile, of men, of beasts, and of all thing that

shamefast: modest

144

men would desire to wit and know. And what man looked in the glass, had he any disease, pricking or motes, smart, or pearls in his eyes, he should be anon healed of it. Such great virtue has the glass. Is it then wonder if I be moved and angry for to lose such manner jewels. The tree in which this glass stood was light and fast and was named cetyne. It should endure ever ere it would rot or worms should hurt it. And therefore King Solomon sealed his temple with the same wood withinforth. Men prized it dearer than fine gold. It is like to the tree of hebenus, of which wood King Crompart[211] made his horse of tree for love of King Morcadigas's daughter, that was so fair, whom he had weened for to have won. The horse was so made within that whosomever rode on it, if he would, he should be within less than an hour a hundred miles thence. And that was well proved, for Cleomedes, the king's son, would not believe that that horse of tree had such virtue. He was young, lusty, and hardy and desired to do great deeds of prize for to be renowned in this world, and leapt on this horse of tree. Crompart turned a pin that stood on his breast and anon the horse lifted him up and went out of the hall by the window. And ere one might say his pater noster, he was gone more ten mile away. Cleomedes was sore afraid and supposed never to have turned again, as the history thereof tells more plainly; but how great dread he had and how far that he rode upon that horse made of the tree of hebenus ere he could know the art and craft how he should turn him and how joyful he was when he knew it and how men sorrowed for him and how he knew all this and the joy thereof when he came again, all this I pass over for losing of time. But the most part of all came to by the virtue of the wood.[212]

"Of which wood the tree that the glass stood in was made

tree: wood   *cetyne*: shittim wood   *hebenus*: ebony

145

and that was withoutforth of the glass half a foot broad, wherein stood some strange mysteries²¹³ which were of gold, of sable, of silver, of yellow, azure, cinnabar. These six colors were therein wrought in such wise as it behooved and under every history the words were graven and enamelled that every man might understand what each history was. After my judgment there was never mirror so costly, so lustly, nor so pleasant. In the beginning stood there a horse made fat, strong, and sore envious upon a hart which ran in the field so far and swiftly that the horse was angry that he ran so far tofore him and could not overtake him. He thought he should catch him and subdue him though he should suffer much pain therefor. The horse spoke tho to a herdsman in this wise, 'If you could take a hart that I well can show you, you should have great profit thereof. You should sell dear his horns, his skin, and his flesh.' The herdsman said, 'How may I come by him?' The horse said, 'Sit upon me and I shall bear you and we shall hunt him till he be taken.' The herdsman sprang and sat upon the horse and saw the hart and he rode after. But the hart was light of foot and swift and outran the horse far.

"They hunted so far after him that the horse was weary and said to the herdsman that sat on him, 'Now sit off. I will rest me. I am all weary and give me leave to go from you.' The herdsman said, 'I have arrested you. You may not escape from me. I have a bridle on your head and spurs on my heels. You shall never have thank hereof.²¹⁴ I shall bedwing and subdue you, had you sworn the contrary.' See how the horse brought himself in thralldom and was taken in his own net. How may one better be taken than by his own proper envy, suffer himself to be taken and ridden? There be many that labor to hurt other and they themselves be hurt and rewarded with the same.

bedwing: subdue

"There was also made an ass and a hound, which dwelled both with a rich man. The man loved his hound well, for he played oft with him as folk do with hounds. The hound lept up and played with his tail and licked his master about the mouth. This saw Boudewin the ass and made great spite thereof in his heart and said to himself 'How may this be and what may my lord see on his foul hound, whom I never see do good nor profit save spring on him and kiss him. But me, whom men put to labor, to bear and draw and do more in a week than he with his fifteen [215] should do in a whole year and yet sits he nevertheless by him at the table and there eats bones, flesh, and fat trenchers. And I have nothing but thistles and nettles and lie on nights on the hard earth and suffer many a scorn. I will no longer suffer this! I will think how I may get my lord's love and friendship like as the hound does.' Therewith came the lord and the ass lifted up his tail and sprang with his forefeet on the lord's shoulders and blared, grinned, and sang and with his feet made two great bules about his ears and put forth his mouth and would have kissed the lord's mouth as he had seen the hound do. Tho cried the lord sore afraid, 'Help! Help! This ass will slay me!' Then came his servants with good staves and smote and beat the ass so sore that he had weened he should have lost his life. Tho returned he to his stable and ate thistles and nettles and was an ass as he tofore was.

"In like wise whoso have envy and spite of another's welfare and were served in like wise, it should be well behoveful. Therefore it is concluded that the ass shall eat thistles and nettles and bear the sack. Though men would do him worship, he cannot understand it, but must use old and lewd manners. Whereas asses get lordships, there men see seldom good rule,

bules: swellings *behoveful*: useful

for they take heed of nothing but on their singular profit. Yet be they taken up and risen great, the more pity is!

"Harken further how my father and Tibert the cat went together and had sworn by their truth that for love nor hate they should not depart and what they got they should depart, to each the half. Then on a time they saw hunters coming over the fields with many hounds. They leapt and ran fast from themward all that they might, as they that were afraid of their life.

" 'Tibert,' said the fox, 'whither shall we now flee? The hunters have espied us! Know you any help?' My father trusted on the promise that each made to other and that he would for no need depart from him. 'Tibert,' said he, 'I have a sack full of wiles, if we have need. As far as we abide together, we need not to doubt hunters nor hounds.'

"Tibert began to sigh and was sore afraid and said, 'Reynard, what avail many words? I know but one wile and thither must I to.' And tho climbed he upon a high tree into the top under the leaves, whereas hunter nor hound might do him no harm and left my father alone in jeopardy of his life. For the hunters set on him the hounds all that they could. Men blew the horns and cried and hallooed the fox 'Slay and take!' When Tibert the cat saw that, he mocked and scorned my father and said, 'What, Reynard cousin, unbind now your sack where all the wiles be in! It is now time. You be so wise called, help yourself, for you have need.'

"This much must my father hear of him to whom he had most his trust on and was almost taken and nigh his death. And he ran and fled with great fear of his life and let his mail slide off because he would be the lighter. Yet all that could not help him, for the hounds were too swift and should have bitten him

depart: divide

148

but he had one adventure that thereby he found an old hole wherein he crept and escaped thus the hunters and hounds.

"Thus held this false deceiver Tibert his sikerness that he had promised. Alas, how many be there nowadays that keep not their promise and set not thereby though they break it. And though I hate Tibert herefor is it wonder but I do not sikerly? [216] I love my soul too well thereto. Nevertheless, if I saw him in adventure and misfall in his body or in his goods, I trow it should not much go to my heart so that another did it.[217] Nevertheless, I shall neither hate him nor have envy at him. I shall for God's love forgive him. Yet is it not so clear out of my heart but a little ill will to himward abides therein as this comes to my remembrance and the cause is that the sensuality of my flesh fights against reason.

"There stood also in that mirror of the wolf, how he found once upon a heath a dead horse flayed. But all the flesh was eaten. Then went he and bit great morsels of the bones that for hunger he took three or four at once and swallowed them in. For he was so greedy that one of the bones stuck thwart in his mouth, whereof he had great pain and was in great fear of his life. He sought all about for wise masters and surgeons and promised great gifts for to be healed of his disease. At the last when he could nowhere find remedy, he came to the crane with his long neck and bill and prayed him to help him and he would love and reward him so well that he should ever be the better. The crane harked after this great reward and put his head into his throat and brought out the bone with his bill.

"The wolf started aside with the plucking and cried out, 'Alas, you do me harm! But I forgive it you. Do no more so. I would not suffer it of any other.'

"The crane said, 'Sir Isegrim, go and be merry for you be all whole. Now give to me that you promised.'

misfall: misfortune

149

"The wolf said, 'Will you hear what he says? I am he that
has suffered and have cause to plain and he will have good of
me! He thanks not me of the kindness that I did to him. He
put his head in my mouth and I have suffered him to draw it
out without hurting. And he did to me also harm and if any
here should have a reward, it should be I by right.'

"Thus the unkind men nowadays reward them that do them
good. When the false and subtle arise and become great, then
go worship and profit all to nought. There be many of right
that ought reward and make amends themselves. Therefore
it is said, and truth it is, who that will chide or chastise, see
that he be clear himself.

"All this and much more than I now can well remember
was made and wrought in this glass. The master that ordained
it was a cunning man and a profound clerk in many sciences.
And because these jewels were overgood and precious for
me to keep and have, therefore I sent them to my dear lord the
king and to the queen in present. Where be they now that give
to their lords such presents? The sorrow that my two children
made when I sent away the glass was great, for they were
woned to look therein and see themselves, how their clothing
and array became them on their bodies. Oh, alas! I knew not
that Cuwart the hare was so nigh his death when I delievered
him the mail with these jewels. I wist not to whom I might
better have taken them, though it should cost me my life, than
him and Bellin the ram. They were two of my best friends.
Out, alas, I cry upon the murderer! I shall know who it was,
though I should run through all the world to seek him. For
murder abides not hidden; it shall come out. Peradventure he
is in this company that knows where Cuwart is become,
though he tell it not. For many false shrews walk with good

ordained: contrived

150

men, from whom no man can keep him. They know their craft so well and can well cover their falseness. But the most wonder that I have is that my lord the king here says so felly that my father nor I did him never good. That thinks me marvel of the king. But there come so many things tofore him that he forgets that one with that other and so fares by me.

"Dear lord, remember not you when my lord your father lived, and you a youngling of two years were, that my father came from school from Montpelier, whereas he had five year studied in recipes and medicines. He knew all the tokens of the urine as well as his hand and also all the herbs and nature of them, which were viscose or laxative. He was a singular master in that science. He might well wear cloth of silk and a gilt girdle. When he came to court, he found the king in great sickness, whereof he was sorry in his heart; for he loved him above all other lords. The king would not forgo him; for when he came, all others had leave to walk where they would. He trusted none so much as him.

"He said, 'Reynard, I am sick and feel me the longer the worst.'

"My father said, 'My dear lord, here is a urinal. Make your water therein and as soon as I may see it I shall tell you what sickness it is and also how you shall be helped.'

"The king did as he counselled him, for he trusted no man better that lived, though so were [218] that my father did not as he should have done to you, but that was by counsel of evil and foul beasts — I had wonder thereof. But it was a rasing against his death.[219] He said, 'My lord, if you will be whole you must eat the liver of a wolf of seven year old. That may you not leave or else you shall die. For your urine shows it plainly.'

felly: cruelly   *recipes*: prescriptions

151

"The wolf stood by and said nought.

"But the king said to him, 'Sir Isegrim, now you hear well that I must have your liver if I will be whole.'

"Tho answered the wolf and said, 'Nay, my lord, not so! I wot well I am not yet five year old. I have heard my mother say so.'

"My father said, 'What skills these words? Let him be opened and I shall know by the liver if it be good for you or not.' And therewith the wolf was had to the kitchen and his liver taken out, which the king ate and was anon all whole of all his sickness. Then thanked he my father much and commanded all his household upon their lives that after that time they should call him Master Reynard.

"He abode still by the king and was believed of all things and must always go by his side. And the king gave to him a garland of roses, which he must always wear on his head. But now this is all turned! All the good things that he did be forgotten and these covetous and ravenous shrews be taken up and set on the high bench and be heard and made great. And the wise folk be put aback, by which these lords oft lack [220] and cause them to be in much trouble and sorrow. For when a covetous man of low birth is made a lord and is much great and above his neighbors has power and might, then he knows not himself nor whence he is come and has no pity on no man's hurt nor hears no man's request, but if he have great gifts. All his intent and desire is to gather good and to be greater. Oh how many covetous men be now in lord's courts! They flatter and smeke and please the prince for their singular avail. But and the prince had need of them or their good, they should rather suffer him to die or fare right hard ere they would give or lene him. They be like the wolf that had liefer the king

skills: means   *smeke*: flatter   *lene*: bestow something on

had died than he would give him his liver. Yet had I liefer, ere that the king or the queen should fare amiss, that twenty such wolves should lose their lives. It were also the least lost. My lord, all this befell in your youth that my father did thus. I trow you have forgotten it.

"And also I have myself done you reverence, worship, and courtesy, unroused [221] be it. Though you now thank me but little, but peradventure you remembered not that I shall now say, not to any forwitting of you, for you be worthy all worship and reverence that any man can do. That have you of almighty God by inheritance of your noble progenitors, wherefore I your humble subject and servant am bound to do to you all the service that I can or may. I came on a time walking with the wolf Isegrim and we had gotten under us both a swine. And for his loud crying, we bit him to death. And sire, you came from far out of a grove against us. You saluted us friendly and said we were welcome and that you and my lady the queen, which came after you, had great hunger and had nothing for to eat and prayed us for to give you part of our winning. Isegrim spoke so soft that a man uneath might hear him, but I spoke out and said, 'Yes, my lord, with a good will! Though it were more, we will well that you have part.' And then the wolf departed as he was wont to do, departed and took that one half for himself and he gave you a quarter, for you and for the queen. That other quarter he ate and bit as hastily as he might, because he would eat it alone. And he gave to me but half the lungs, that I pray God that evil mote he fare!

"Thus showed he his conditions and nature. Ere men should have sung a credo, you, my lord, had eaten your part. And yet would you fain have had more, for you were not full. And

forwitting: reproach   *under*: between   *conditions*: personal qualities

153

because he gave you no more nor proffered you, you lifted up your right foot and smote him between the ears that you tore his skin over his eyes; and tho he might no longer abide, but he bled, howled, and ran away and left his part there lie. Tho said you to him, 'Haste you again hither and bring to us more. And hereafter see better how you deal and part.'

"Then said I, 'My lord, if it please you, I will go with him.' I wot well what you said. I went with him. He bled and groaned, as sore as he was, all softly; he dared not cry loud. We went so far that we brought a calf. And when you saw us come therewith, you laughed for you were well pleased. You said to me that I was swift in hunting; 'I see well that you can find well when you take it upon you. You be good to send forth in a need. The calf is good and fat. Hereof shall you be the dealer.'

"I said, 'My lord, with a good will! The one half, my lord, shall be for you and the other half for my lady the queen. The muggets, liver, lungs, and the inwards shall be for your children. The head shall Isegrim the wolf have and I will have the feet.'

"Tho said you, 'Reynard, who has taught you to depart so courteously?'

" 'My lord,' said I, 'that has done this priest that sits here with a bloody crown. He lost his skin with the uncourteous departing of the swine and for his covetous and ravin he has hurt and shame.'

"Alas, there be many wolves nowadays that without right and reason destroy and eat them that they may have the over-hand of. They spare neither flesh nor blood, friend nor enemy. What they can get, that take they. Oh woe be to that land and to towns whereas the wolves have the overhand!

muggets: intestines   *ravin*: gluttony

"My lord, this and many other good things have I done for you that I could well tell if it were not too long, of which now you remember little by the words that I hear of you. If you would all thing oversee well, you would not say as you do. I have seen the day that there should no great matter be concluded in this court without my advice. Albeit that this adventure is now fallen, it might happen yet that my words shall be heard and also believed as well as another's, as far as right will, for I desire no other. For if there be any can say and make good by sufficient witnesses that I have trespassed, I will abide all the right and law that may come thereof. And if any say on me anything of which he can bring no witnesses, let me then be ruled after the law and custom of this court."

The king said, "Reynard, you say reasonably. I know not of Cuwart's death more than that Bellin the ram brought his head here in the mail. Thereof I let you go quit, for I have no witness thereof."

"My dear lord," said [Reynard],[222] "God thank you! Sikerly you do well, for his death makes me so sorrowful that methinks my heart will break in two. Oh when they departed from me, my heart was so heavy that methought I should have swooned. I wot well it was a token of the loss that tho was so nigh coming to me."

All the most part of them that were there and heard the fox's words of the jewels and how he made his countenance and stretched him [223] had verily supposed that it had not been feigned, but that it had been true. They were sorry of his loss and misadventure and also of his sorrow. The king and the queen had both pity of him and bade him to make not too much sorrow, but that he should endeavor him to seek them. For he had so much praised them that they had great will and desire to have them and because he had made them to understand that he had sent these jewels to them. Though they never had them, yet they thanked him and prayed him to help that they might have them.

The fox understood their meaning well. He thought toward them but little good for all that. He said, "God thank you, my lord and my lady that you so friendly comfort me in my sorrow. I shall not rest night nor day nor all they that will do anything for me, but run and pray, threaten and ask all the four corners of the world, though I should ever seek till that I know where they be become. And I pray you, my lord the king, that if they were in such place as I could not get them by prayer, by might, nor by request, that you would assist me and abide by me, for it touches yourself and the good is yours. And also it is your part to do justice on theft and murder, which both be in this case."

"Reynard," said the king, "that shall I not leave when you know where they be. My help shall be always ready for you."

"Oh dear lord, this is too much presented to me! If I had power and might, I should deserve against you." [224]

Now has the fox his matter fast and fair, for he has the king in his hand as he would. Him thought that he was in better case than it was like to have been. He has made so many lesings that he may go freely where he will without complaining of any of them all.

Save of Isegrim, which was to himwards angry and displeased, and said, "Oh noble king, are you so much childish that you believe this false and subtle shrew and suffer yourself with false lies thus to be deceived? Of faith, it should be long or I should believe him! He is in murder and treason all bewrapped and he mocks you tofore your visage. I shall tell him another tale. I am glad that I see now him here. All his lesings shall not avail him ere he depart from me.

leave: neglect

156

xxxiii. *How Isegrim the Wolf Complained Again on the Fox*

"My lord, I pray you to take heed. This false thief betrayed my wife once, foul and dishonestly. It was so that in a winter's day that they went together through a great water and he bore my wife on hand [225] that he would teach her to take fish with her tail and that she should let it hang in the water a good while and there should so much fish cleave on it that four of them should not con eat it.

"The fool my wife supposed he had said truth and she went in the mire to the belly too, ere she came into the water. And when she was in the deepest of the water, he bade her hold her tail till that the fish were come. She held her tail so long that it was frozen hard in the ice and could not pluck it out. And when he saw that he sprang up after on her body. Alas there ravished he and forced my wife so knavishly that I am ashamed to tell it. She could not defend herself, the silly beast, she stood so deep in the mire. Hereof he cannot say nay, for I found him with the deed. For as I went above upon the bank, I saw him beneath upon my wife shouting and sticking as men do when they do such work and play. Alas, what pain suffered I tho at my heart. I had almost for sorrow lost my five wits and cried as loud as I might 'Reynard, what do you there!' And when he saw me so nigh, tho leapt he off and went his way.

"I went to her in great heaviness. And went deep in that mire and that water ere I could break the ice. And much pain suffered she ere she could have out her tail and yet left a gobbet of her tail behind her. And we were like both thereby to have lost our lives, for she galped and cried so loud for the smart that she had ere she came out that the men of the village came out with staves and bills, with flails and pitchforks, and

gobbet: chunk *galped*: yelped *bills*: pickaxes

157

the wives with their distaffs and cried dispiteously 'Slay, slay!' and 'Smite down right!' I was never in my life so afraid, for uneath we escaped. We ran so fast that we sweat. There was a villain that stuck on us with a pike, which hurt us sore. He was strong and swift of foot. Had it not been night certainly we had been slain. The foul old queans would fain have beaten us. They said that we had bitten their sheep. They cursed us with many a curse. Tho came we in a field full of broom and brambles; there hid we us from the villains. And they dared not follow us further by night but returned home again. See, my lord, this foul matter! This is murder, rape, and treason, which you ought to do justice thereon sharply."

Reynard answered and said, "If this were true, it should go too nigh my honor and worship! God forbid that it should be found true! It is well true that I taught her how she should in a place catch fish and showed her a good way for to go over into the water without going into the mire. But she ran so desirously when she heard me name the fish that she neither way nor path held, but went into the ice, wherein she was forfrozen. And that was because she abode too long. She had fish enough if she could have been pleased with measure. It falls oft who that would have all loses all. Overcovetousness was never good, for the beast cannot be satisfied. And when I saw her in the ice so fast I went to have helped her and heaved and shoved and stuck here and there to have brought her out. But it was all pain lost, for she was too heavy for me. Tho came Isegrim and saw how I shoved and stuck and did all my best. And he, as a foul churl, foul and ribaldrously slanders me with her, as these foul unthrifts be wont to do. But, my dear lord, it was no otherwise. He belies me falsely. Peradventure his

dispiteously: mercilessly   *queans*: sluts   *forfrozen*: frozen fast
unthrifts: no goods

158

eyes dazzled as he looked from above down. He cried and
cursed me and swore many an oath I should dear aby it. When
I heard him so curse and threaten, I went my way and let him
curse and menace till he was weary. And tho went he and
heaved and shoved and helped his wife out and then he leapt
and ran and she also for to get them aheat and to warm them
or else they should have died for cold. And whatsomever I
have said afore or after, that is clearly all truth. I would not
for a thousand mark of fine gold lie to you one lesing. It were
not fitting for me. Whatsomever fall of me, I shall say the
truth like as my elders have always done sith the time that we
first understood reason. And if you be in doubt of anything
that I have said otherwise than truth, give me respite of eight
days that I may have counsel and I shall bring such information with good, true, and sufficient record that you shall all
your life during trust and believe me and so shall all your
council also. What have I to do with the wolf? It is tofore
clearly enough shown that he is a foul, villainous caitiff and
an unclean beast when he dealt and departed the swine. So
is it now known to you all by his own words that [he] is a
defamer of women as much as in him is. You may well mark
everyone who should lust to do that game to one so steadfast
a wife being in so great peril of death. Now ask you his wife
if it be so as he says. If she will say the truth, I wot well she
shall say as I do."

Tho spoke Erswind, the wolf's wife, "Ach, fell Reynard,
no man can keep himself from you; you can so well utter
your words and your falsenesses and reason set forth. But it
shall be evil rewarded in the end.

"How brought you me once into the well where the two
buckets hung by one cord running through one pulley, which
went one up and another down! You sat in that one bucket

dazzled: clouded-over

159

beneath in the pit in great dread. I came thither and heard you sigh and make sorrow and asked you how that you came there. You said that you had there so many good fishes eaten out of the water that your belly would break. I said, 'Tell me how I shall come to you.' Then said you, 'Aunt, spring into that bucket that hangs there and you shall come anon to me.' I did so and I went downward and you came upward. Tho was I all angry. You said, 'Thus fares the world! That one goes up and another goes down.' Tho sprang you forth and went your way and I abode there alone sitting a whole day sore ahungered and acold. And thereto had I many a stroke ere I could get thence."

"Aunt," said the fox, "though the strokes did you harm, I had liefer you had them than I, for you may better bear them. For one of us must needs have had them. I taught you good. Would you understand it and think on it that you another time take better heed and believe no man overhastily, is he friend or cousin, for every man seeks his own profit. They be now fools that do not so and specially when they be in jeopardy of their lives."

xxxiv. *A Fair Parable of the Fox and the Wolf*

"My lord," said Dame Erswind, "I pray you hear how he can blow with all winds [226] and how fair brings he his matters forth."

"Thus has he brought me many times in scathe and hurt," said the wolf. "He has once betrayed me to the she-ape, my aunt, where I was in great dread and fear, for I left there almost my one ear. If the fox will tell it how it befell, I will give him the fordeal thereof, for I cannot tell it so well but he shall berisp me."

"Well," said the fox, "I shall tell it without stammering. I

fordeal: opportunity   *berisp*: censure

shall say the truth. I pray you harken me. He came into the wood and complained to me that he had great hunger. For I saw him never so full, but he would always have had fain more. I have great wonder where the meat becomes that he destroys. I see now on his countenance that he begins to grim for hunger. When I heard him so complain I had pity of him and I said I was also hungry. Then went we half a day together and found nothing. Tho whined he and cried and said he might go no further. Then espied I a great hole standing in the midst under a haw which was thick of brambles. And I heard a rushing therein. I wist not what it was.

"Then said I, 'Go therein and look if there be anything there for us. I wot well there is somewhat.'

"Tho said he, 'Cousin, I would not creep into that hole for twenty pounds but I wist first what is therein. Me thinks that there is some perilous thing. But I shall abide here under this tree, if you will go therein tofore. But come anon again and let me weet what thing is therein. You can many a subtlety and can well help yourself and much better than I.' See, my lord the king, thus he made me, poor wight, to go tofore into the danger and he which is great, long, and strong abode without and rested him in peace. Await if I did not for him there! [227]

"I would not suffer the dread and fear that I there suffered for all the good in earth but if I wist how to escape. I went hardily in. I found the way dark, long, and broad. Ere I right in the hole came, so espied I a great light which came in from that other side. There lay a great ape with twain great wide eyes and they glimmed as a fire. And she had a great mouth with long teeth and sharp nails on her feet and on her hands. I weened it had been a marmoset, a baboon, or a meercat. For I saw never fouler beast and by her lay three of her children,

glimmed: glimmered   *meercat*: monkey

161

which were right foul for they were right like the mother. When they saw me come, they gaped wide on me and were all still. I was afraid and would well that I had been thence. But I thought, 'I am therein. I must therethrough and come out as well I may.' As I saw her methought she seemed more than Isegrim the wolf and her children were more than I. I saw never a fouler meinie. They lay on foul hay, which was all bepissed. They were beslobbered and beclogged to their ears too in their own dung. It stank that I was almost smoldered. Thereof I dared not say but good.

"And then I said, 'Aunt, God give you good day and all my cousins, your fair children. They be of their age the fairest that ever I saw. Oh lord God, how well please they me! How lovely, how fair be they! Each of them for their beauty might be a great king's son. Of right we ought to thank you that you thus increase our lineage. Dear Aunt, when I heard say that you were delivered and laid down,[228] I could no longer abide, but must come and friendly visit you. I am sorry that I had not erst known it.'

" 'Reynard cousin,' said she, 'you be welcome. For that you have found me and thus come to see me, I thank you. Dear cousin, you be right true and named right wise in all lands. And also that you gladly further and bring your lineage in great worship, you must teach my children with the yours some wisdom that they may know what they shall do and leave. I have thought on you, for gladly you go and fellowship with the good.' Oh how well was I pleased when I heard these words. This deserved I at the beginning when I called her aunt, howbeit that she was nothing sib to me; for my right aunt is Dame Rukenaw, that yonder stands, which is woned to bring forth wise children.

meinie: household   *smoldered*: smothered   *erst*: sooner

"I said, 'Aunt, my life and my good is at your command-ment and what I may do for you by night and by day. I will gladly teach them all that I can.'

"I would fain have been thence for the stench of them and also I had pity of the great hunger that Isegrim had. I said,

He was a cloisterer or a closed recluse become

'Aunt, I shall commit you and your fair children to God and take my leave. My wife shall think long after me.' [229]

" 'Dear cousin,' said she, 'you shall not depart till you have eaten. For if you did, I would say you were not kind.' Tho

163

stood she up and brought me in another hole whereas was much meat of harts and hinds, roes, pheasants, partridges, and much other venison that I wondered from whence all this meat might come. And when I had eaten my bellyfull, she gave me a great piece of a hind for to eat with my wife and with my household when I came home. I was ashamed to take it, but I might no otherwise do. I thanked her and took my leave. She bade me I should come soon again. I said I would and so departed thence merrily that I so well had sped.

"I hasted me out and when I came and saw Isegrim, which lay groaning, and I asked him how he fared, he said, 'Nephew, all evil, for it is wonder that I live. Bring you any meat to eat? I die for hunger!' Tho had I compassion of him and gave him that I had and saved him there his life, whereof then [he] thanked me greatly, howbeit that he now owes me evil will.

"He had eaten this up anon. Tho said he, 'Reynard, dear cousin, what found you in that hole? I am more hungry now that I was tofore. My teeth be now sharpened to eat.'

"I said then, 'Eme, haste you then lightly into that hole. You shall find there enough. There lies my aunt with her children. If you will spare the truth and lie great lesings, you shall have there all your desire. But and you say truth, you shall take harm.'

"My lord, was not this enough said and warned, whoso would understand it, that all that he found he should say the contrary? But rude and plump beasts cannot understand wisdom; therefore hate they all subtle inventions, for they cannot conceive them. Yet, nevertheless, he said he would go in and lie so many lesings ere he should mishap that all men should have wonder of it. And so went forth into that foul stinking hole and found the marmoset. She was like the devil's daughter and on her children hung much filth clotted in gobbets.

conceive: apprehend

"Tho cried he, 'Alas, me growls of [230] these false nickers! Come they out of hell? Men may make devils afraid of them! Go and drown them that evil mote they fare. I saw never fouler worms. They make all my hair to stand right up.'

" 'Sir Isegrim,' said she, 'what may I do thereto? [231] They be my children and I must be their mother. What lies that in your way [232] whether they be foul or fair? They have you nothing cost. Here has been one today before you which was to them nigh of kin and was your better and wiser and he said that they were fair. Who has sent you hither with these tidings?'

" 'Dame, will you wit, I will eat some of your meat. It is better bestowed on me than on these foul wights.'

"She said, 'Here is no meat.'

"He said, 'Here is enough.' And therewith he started with his head toward the meat and would have gone into the hole where the meat was. But my aunt started up with her children and ran to him with their sharp long nails so sore that the blood ran over his eyes. I heard him cry, swear, and howl; but I know of no defense that he made but that he ran fast out of the hole. And he was there cratched and bitten and many a hole had they made in his coat and skin. His visage was all on a blood and almost he had lost his one ear. He groaned and complained to me sore. Then asked I him if he had well lied.

"He said, 'I said like as I saw and found and that was a foul bitch with many foul wights.'

" 'Nay, eme,' said I, 'you should have said, "Fair niece, how fare you and your fair children, which be my well-beloved cousins?" '

"The wolf said, 'I had liefer that they were hanged ere I that said.'

nickers: water monsters

165

" 'Yea, eme, therefore must you receive such manner payment. It is better otherwhile to lie than to say truth. They that be better, wiser, and stronger than we be have done so tofore us.' See, my lord the king, thus got he his red coif. Now stands he all so simply as he knew no harm. I pray you ask you him if it was not thus. He was not far off, if I wot it well."

xxxv. *How Isegrim Proffered His Glove to the Fox*

The wolf said, "I may well forbear your mocks and your scorns and also your fell venomous words, strong thief that you are. You said that I was almost dead for hunger when you helped me in my need. That is falsely lied. For it was but a bone that you gave to me. You had eaten away all the flesh that was thereon. And you mock me and say that I am hungry here where I stand. That touches my worship too nigh. What many a spitey word have you brought forth with false lesings and that I have conspired the king's death for the treasure that you have said to him is in Hulsterloo. And you have also my wife shamed and slandered that she shall never recover it and I should ever be disworshipped thereby if I avenged it not. I have forborne you long, but now you shall not escape me. I cannot make here of great proof.[233] But I say heretofore my lord and tofore all them that be here that you are a false traitor and a murderer. And that shall I prove and make good on your body within lists in the field and that body against body. And then shall our strife have an end. And thereto I cast to thee my glove. And take you it up, I shall have right of you or die therefor!"

Reynard the fox thought, "How come I on this camping?

coif: skullcap	*strong*: flagrant	*spitey*: spiteful
disworshipped: disgraced	*forborne*: tolerated	*lists*: barriers
	camping: fighting	

We be not both like. I shall not well con stand against this strong thief. All my proof [234] is now come to an end."

XXXVI. *How the Fox Took Up the Glove and How the King Set to Them Day and Field for to Come and Do Their Battle*

Yet thought the fox, "I have good advantage. The claws of his forefeet be off and his feet be yet sore thereof when for my sake he was unshoed. He shall be somewhat the weaker."

Then said the fox, "Who that says that I am a traitor or a murderer, I say he lies falsely and that are you specially, Isegrim. You bring me there as I would be. This have I oft desired. Lo, here is my pledge that all your words be false and that I shall defend me and make good that you lie."

The king received the pledges and admitted the battle and asked borrows of them both that on the morn they should come and perform their battle and do as they ought to do. Then the bear and the cat were borrows for the wolf and for the fox were borrows Grimbert the dasse and Bitelouse.

XXXVII. *How Rukenaw the She-ape Counselled the Fox How He Should Behave Him in the Field Against the Wolf*

The she-ape said to the fox, "Reynard nephew, see that you take heed in your battle. Be cold and wise. Your eme taught me once a prayer that is of much virtue to him that shall fight. And a great master and a wise clerk and was Abbot of Boudelo [235] that taught him; he said who that said devoutly this prayer fasting shall not that day be overcome in battle nor in fighting. Therefore, dear nephew, be not afraid. I shall read it over you tomorrow. Then may you be sure enough of the wolf. It is better to fight than to have the neck asunder."

borrows: pledges

167

"I thank you, dear aunt," said the fox. "The quarrel that I have is rightful. Therefore I hope I shall speed well and that shall greatly be my help."

All his lineage abode by him all the night and helped him to drive away the time. Dame Rukenaw the she-ape, his aunt, thought always on his profit and fordeal. And she did all his hair from the head to the tail be shorn off smooth and she anointed all his body with oil of olive. And then was his body also glat [236] and slipper that the wolf should have no hold on him and he was round and fat also on his body.

And she said to him, "Dear cousin, you must now drink much that tomorrow you may the better make your urine, but you shall hold it in till you come to the field. And when need is and time, so shall you piss full your row tail and smite the wolf therewith in his beard. And if you might hit him therewith in his eyes, then shall you beneme him his sight. That should much hinder him. But else hold always your tail fast between your legs that he catch you not thereby and hold down your ears lying plat after your head that he hold you not thereby. And see wisely to yourself and at beginning flee from his strokes. And let him spring and run after you and run tofore whereas most dust is and stir it with your feet that it may flee in his eyes and that shall much hinder his sight. And while he rubs his eyes, take your advantage and smite and bite him there as you may most hurt him. And always to hit him with your tail full of piss in his visage and that shall make him so woe that he shall not wit where he is. And let him run after you for to make him weary. Yet his feet be sore of that you made him to lose his shoes. And though he be great, he has no heart. Nephew, certainly this is my counsel. The cunning goes tofore strength. Therefore see for yourself and set yourself

slipper: slippery   *row*: rough   *beneme*: take from

wisely at the defense that you and we all may have worship thereof. I would be sorry if you mishapped. I shall teach you the words that your eme Martin taught me that you may overcome your enemy, as I hope you shall do without doubt."

Therewith she laid her hand upon his head and said these words, " 'Blaerde shay alpheino kasbue gorfons alsbuifrio.' Nephew, now be you sure from all mischief and dread and counsel you that you rest you a little, for it is by the day. You shall be the better disposed. We shall awake you in all in time."

"Aunt," said the fox, "I am now glad. God thank you, you have done to me such good I can never deserve it fully again. Methinks there may nothing hurt me sith that you have said these holy words over me."

Then went he and laid him down under a tree in the grass and slept till the sun was risen. Tho came the otter and waked him and bade him arise and gave him a good young duck and said, "Dear cousin, I have this night made many a leap in the water ere I could get this young fat duck. I have taken it from a fowler. Take and eat it."

Reynard said, "This is good handsel.[237] If I refuse, I were a fool. I thank you, cousin, that you remember me. If I live, I shall reward you." The fox ate the duck without sauce or bread. It savored him well and went well in. And he drank thereto four great draughts of water. Then went to the battleward and all they that loved him went with him.

xxxviii. *How the Fox Came Into the Field and How They Fought*

When the king saw Reynard thus shorn and oiled he said to him, "Eigh, fox, how well can you see for yourself!" He wondered thereof he was so foul to look on. But the fox said not

169

one word, but kneeled down low to the earth unto the king and to the queen and struck him forth into the field.

The wolf was there ready and spoke many a proud word. The rulers and keepers of the field were [238] the leopard and the loss. They brought forth the book on which swore the wolf that the fox was a traitor and a murderer and none might be falser than he was and that he would prove on his body and make it good. Reynard the fox swore that he lied as a false knave and a cursed thief and that he would do good on his body.

When this was done, the governors of the field bade them do their devoir. Then roomed they all the field save Dame Rukenaw the she-ape. She abode by the fox and bade him remember well the words that she had said to him.

She said, "See well to! When you were seven years old, you were wise enough to go by night without lantern or moonshine. Where you wist to win any good, you be named among the people wise and subtle. Pain yourself to work so that you win the prize. Then may you have every honor and worship and all we that be your friends."

He answered, "My dearest aunt, I know it well. I shall do my best and think on your counsel. I hope so to do that all my lineage shall have worship thereby and my enemies shame and confusion."

She said, "God grant it you!"

xxxix. *How the Fox and the Wolf Fought Together*

Therewith she went out of the field and let them twain go together. The wolf tread forth to the fox in great wrath and opened his forefeet and supposed to have taken the fox in them. But the fox sprang from him lightly, for he was lighter to foot

loss: lynx   *devoir*: duty

than he. The wolf sprang after and hunted the fox sore. Their friends stood without the lists and looked upon them. The wolf strode wider than Reynard did and oft overtook him and lifted up his foot and weened to have smote him. But the fox saw to and smote him with his row tail, which he had all bepissed, in his visage. Tho weened the wolf to have been plat blind. The piss started into his eyes. Then must he rest for to make clean his eyes. Reynard thought on his fordeal and stood above the wind scrabbing and casting with his feet the dust that it flew the wolf's eyes full. The wolf was sore blinded therewith in such wise that he must leave the running after him, for the sand and piss cleaved under his eyes that it smarted so sore that he must rub and wash it away.

Tho came Reynard in a great anger and bit him three great wounds on his head with his teeth and said, "What is that, sir wolf? Has one there bitten you? How is it with you? I will all otherwise on you yet. Abide! I shall bring you some new thing. You have stolen many a lamb and destroyed many a simple beast and now falsely have appealed me and brought me in this trouble. All this shall I now avenge on you. I am chosen to reward you for your old sins, for God will no longer suffer you in your great ravin and shrewdness. I shall now assoil you and that shall be good for your soul. Take patiently this penance, for you shall live no longer. The hell shall be your purgatory. Your life is now in my mercy, but and if you will kneel down and ask me forgiveness and knowledge you to be overcome. Yet though you be evil, yet I will spare you. For my conscience counsels me I should not gladly slay no man."

Isegrim weened with these mocking and spitous words to have gone out of his wit: and that dared [239] him so much that

plat: quite	*scrabbing*: clawing	*knowledge*: acknowl-
spitous: spiteful		edge

he wist not what to say buff nor haff [240] he was so angry in his heart. The wounds that Reynard had given him bled and smarted sore and he thought how he might best avenge it.

With great anger he lifted up his foot and smote the fox on the head so great a stroke that he fell to the ground. Tho started the wolf to and weened to have taken him, but the fox was light and wily and rose lightly up and met with him fiercely and there began a fell battle which dured long. The wolf had great spite on the fox as it well seemed. He sprang after him ten times each after other and would fain have had him fast, but his skin was so slipper and fat of the oil that always he escaped from him. Oh so subtle and snell was the fox that many times when the wolf weened well to be sure of him he started then between his legs and under his belly and then turned he again and gave the wolf a stroke with his tail full of piss in his eyes that Isegrim weened he should have lost his sight. And this did he oftentimes. And always when he had so smitten him, then would he go above the wind and raise the dust that it made his eyes full of stuffs.[241] Isegrim was woebegone and thought he was at an afterdeal, yet was his strength and might much more than the fox's. Reynard had many a sore stroke of him when he raught him. They gave each other many a stroke and many a bite when they saw their advantage. And each of them did his best to destroy the other. I would I might see such a battle! That one was wily and that other was strong. That one fought with strength and that other with subtlety.

The wolf was angry that the fox endured so long against him. If his foremost feet had been whole, the fox had not endured so long. But the sores were so open that he might not well run and the fox might better off and on than he. And also

snell: quick   *afterdeal*: disadvantage

172

he swung his tail with piss oft under his eyes and made him that him thought that his eyes should go out.

At the last he said to himself, "I will make an end of this battle. How long shall this caitiff dure thus against me? I am so great I should if I lay upon him press him to death. It is to me a great shame that I spare him so long. Men shall mock and point me with fingers to my shame and rebuke, for I am yet on the worst side. I am sore wounded. I bleed sore and he drowns me with his piss and casts so much dust and sand in my eyes that hastily I shall not con see if I suffer him any longer. I will set it in adventure and see what shall come thereof."

With that he smote with his foot Reynard on the head that he fell down to the ground; and ere he could arise, he caught him on his feet and lay upon him as he would have pressed him to death. Tho began the fox to be afraid and so were all his friends when they saw him lie under. And on that other side all Isegrim's friends were joyful and glad. The fox defended him fast with his claws as he lay upward with his feet and gave him many a clope. The wolf dared not with his feet do him much harm, but with his teeth snatched at him as he would have bitten him. When the fox saw that he should be bitten and was in great dread he smote the wolf in the head with his foremost claws and tore the skin off between his brows and his ears and that one of his eyes hung out, which did him much pain. He howled. He wept. He cried aloud and made a piteous noise for the blood ran down as it had been a stream.

XL. *How the Fox Being Under the Wolf with Flattering Words Glozed Him That the Fox Came to His Above Again*

The wolf wiped his eyes. The fox was glad when he saw

clope: blow   *glozed*: flattered

THE HISTORY OF REYNARD THE FOX

that. He wrestled so sore that he sprang up on his feet while he rubbed his eyes. The wolf was not well pleased therewithall and smote after him ere he escaped and caught him in his arms and held him fast, not withstanding that he bled. Reynard was woe then. There wrestled they long and sore. The wolf waxed so angry that he forgot all his smart and pain and threw the fox all plat under him, which came him evil to pass. For his one hand by which he defended him started in the falling into Isegrim's throat and then was he afraid to lose his hand.

The wolf said tho to the fox, "Now choose whether you will yield you as overcome or else I shall certainly slay you. The scattering of the dust, your piss, your mocking, nor your defense, nor all your false wiles may not now help you. You may not escape me. You have heretofore done me so much harm and shame and now I have lost my one eye and thereto sore wounded."

When Reynard heard that it stood so rowm [242] that he should choose to knowledge him overcome and yield him or else to take the death, he thought the choice was worth ten mark and that he must say that one or that other. He had anon concluded what he would say and began to say to him with fair words in this wise:

"Dear eme, I will gladly become your man with all my good and I will go for you to the holy grave and shall get pardon and winning for your cloister of all the churches that be in the Holy Land, which shall much profit to your soul and your elders' souls also. I trow there was never such a proffer proffered to any king. And I shall serve you like as I should serve our holy father the Pope. I shall hold of you all that I have and ever be your servant and forth I shall make that all my lineage shall do in likewise. Then shall you be a lord above all lords. Who should then dare do anything against you? And

174

furthermore whatsomever I take of poultry, geese, partridge, or plover, fish or flesh, or whatsomever it be, thereof shall you first have the choice and your wife and your children ere any come in my body. Thereto I will always abide by you that where you be there shall be no hurt nor scathe come to you. You be strong and I am wily. Let us abide together that one with the counsel and that other with the deed. Then may there nothing misfall to usward. And we be so nigh of kin each to other that of right should be no anger between us. I would not have fought against you if I might have escaped, but you appealed me first unto fight. Tho must I do that I not do would gladly. And in this battle I have been courteous to you. I have not yet showed the utterest of my might on you, like as I would have done if you had been a stranger to me. For the nephew ought to spare the eme; it is good reason and it ought to be. Dear eme, so have I now done and that may you mark well. When I ran from you, my heart would not consent thereto; for I might have hurt you much more than I did. But I thought it never, for I have not hurt you nor done you so much harm that may hinder you, save only that mishap that has fallen on your eye. Ach, therefore I am sorry and suffer much sorrow in my heart. I would well, dear eme, that it had not happed you but that it had fallen on me, so that you therewith had been pleased, howbeit that you shall have thereby a great advantage. For when you hereafter sleep you need not to shut but one window where another must shut two. My wife and my children and my lineage shall fall down to your feet before the king and tofore all them that you will desire and pray you humbly that you will suffer Reynard, your nephew, live. And also I shall knowledge oft to have trespassed against you and what lesings I have lied upon you. How might any lord have

appealed: invited

175

more honor than I proffer you? I would for no good do this to another. Therefore I pray you to be pleased herewithall.

"I wot well if you would you might now slay me. But and you so done had, what had you won? So must you ever after this time keep you from my friends and lineage. Therefore he is wise that can in his anger measure himself and not be over-hasty and to see well what may fall or hap afterward to him. What man that in his anger can well advise him, certainly he is wise. Men find many fools that in heat hasten them so much that after they repent them and then it is too late. But, dear eme, I trow that you be too wise so to do. It is better to have prize,[243] honor, rest, and peace and many friends that be ready to help him than to have shame, hurt, unrest, and also many enemies lying in await to do him harm. Also it is little worship to him that has overcome a man then to slay him. It is great shame, not for my life that I were dead; that were a little hurt."

Isegrim the wolf said, "Ay, thief, how fain would you be loosened and discharged from me. That hear I well by your words. Were you now from me on your free feet, you would not set by me an eggshell. Though you promise to me all the world of fine red gold, I would not let you escape. I set little by you and all your friends and lineage. All that you have here said is but lesings and feigned falseness. Ween you thus to de-ceive me? It is long sith that I knew you. I am no bird to be locked nor taken by chaff. I know well enough good corn. Oh how would you mock me if I let you thus escape! You might well have said this to one that knew you not, but to me you lose your flattering and sweet fluting. For I understand too well your subtle lying tales. You have so oft deceived me that me behooves now to take good heed of you. You false stink-

locked: enticed

ing knave, you say that you have spared me in this battle. Look hitherward to me! Is not my one eye out and thereto have you wounded me in twenty places in my head? You would not suffer me so long to rest as to take once my breath. I were overmuch a fool if I should now spare you or be merciful to you so many a confusion and shame as you have done to me. And that also that touches me most of all, that you have disworshipped me and slandered Erswind my wife, whom I love as well as myself and falsely forced and deceived her, which shall never out of my heart. For as oft as it comes to my mind, all my anger and hate that I have to you renews."

In the meanwhile while Isegrim was thus speaking, the fox bethought him how he might help himself and stuck his other hand after between his legs and gripped the wolf fast by the cullions. And he wrung them so sore that for woe and pain he must cry loud and howl. Then the fox drew his other hand out of his mouth. The wolf had so much pain and anguish of the sore wringing that the fox dowed and wrung his genitors and he spit blood and for great pain he beshit himself.

XLI. *How Isegrim the Wolf Was Overcome and How the Battle Was Taken Up and Finished and How the Fox Had the Worship*

This pain did him more sorrow and woe than his eye did, that so sore bled; and also it made him to overthrow [244] all in a swoon, for he had so much bled and also the thrusting that he suffered in his cullions made him so faint that he lost his might. Then Reynard the fox leapt upon him with all his might and caught him by the legs and drew him forth through the field that they all might see it. And he stuck and smote him sore. Then were Isegrim's friends all full of sorrow and went

dowed: squeezed

177

all weeping unto their lord the king and prayed him that he would do cease the battle and take it up into his hand.

The king granted it and then went the keepers of the field, the leopard and the loss, and said to the fox and to the wolf, "Our lord the king will speak with you and will that this battle be ended. He will take it into his hand. He desires that you will give your strife unto him for if any of you here were slain, it should be a great shame on both sides, for you have as much worship of this field as you may have."

And they said to the fox, "All the beasts give to you the prize that have seen the battle."

The fox said, "Thereof I thank them and what that shall please my lord to command, that shall not I gainsay. I desire no better but to have won the field. Let my friends come hither to me. I will take advice of them what I shall do."

They said that they thought it good and also it was reason in weighty matters a man should take advice of his friends. Then came Dame Slopecade and Grimbert the dasse her husband; Dame Rukenaw with her two sisters; Bitelouse and Fullrump, her two sons; and Hatenette, her daughter; the flindermouse; and the weasel. And there came more than twenty which would not have come if the fox had lost the field. So who that wins and comes to his above, he gets great lose and worship; and who that is overthrown and has the worst, to him will no man gladly come. There came also to the fox the beaver; the otter; and both their wives, Patecroet and Ordegale; and the ostrole; the marten; the fitchews; the ferret; the mouse; and the squirrel; and many more than I can name. And all because he had won the field. Yea, some came that tofore had complained on him and were now of his next kin, and they showed him right friendly cheer and countenance. Thus fares

flindermouse: bat   *lose*: renown

178

the world now. Who that is rich and high on the wheel, he has many kinsmen and friends that shall help to bear out his wealth. But who that is needy and in pain or in poverty finds but few friends and kinsmen, for every man almost eschews his company and way.

There was then great feast. They blew up trumpets and piped with shawms. They said all, "Dear nephew, blessed be God that you have sped well. We were in great dread and fear when we saw you lie under."

Reynard the fox thanked all them friendly and received them with great joy and gladness. Then he asked of them what they counselled him, if he should give the field unto the king or no.

Dame Slopecade said, "Yea, hardly cousin. You may with worship well set it into his hands and trust him well enough." Tho went they all with the keepers of the field unto the king and Reynard the fox went tofore them all with trumps and pipes and much other minstrelsy. The fox kneeled down tofore the king.

The king bade him stand up and said to him, "Reynard, you be now joyful. You have kept your day worshipfully. I discharge you and let you go freely quit where it pleases you. And the debate between you I hold it on me and shall discuss it by reason and by counsel of noble men and will ordain thereof that ought be done by reason, at such time as Isegrim shall be whole. And then shall I send for you to come to me. And then by God's grace I shall give out the sentence and judgment."

XLII. *An Example That the Fox Told to the King When He Had Won the Field*

"My worthy and dear lord the king," said the fox, "I am

well agreed and paid therewith. But when I came first into your court, there were many that were fell and envious to me, which never had hurt nor cause of scathe by me. But they thought that they might best over me [245] and all they cried with my enemies against me and would fain have destroyed me because they thought that the wolf was better witholden [246] and greater with you than I was, which am your humble subject. They knew no other thing, why nor wherefore. They thought not as the wise be woned to do — that is, what the end may happen.[247]

"My lord, these be like a great heap of hounds which I once saw stand at a lord's place upon a dunghill, whereas they awaited that men should bring them meat. Then saw they a hound come out of the kitchen and had taken there a fair rib of beef ere it was given him. And he ran fast away with all, but the cook had espied or he went away and took a great bowl full of scalding water and cast it on his hips behind, whereof he thanked nothing the cook. For the hair behind was scalded off and his skin seemed as if it had been through sodden. Nevertheless he escaped away and kept that he had won.

"And when his fellows, the other hounds, saw him come with this fair rib they called him all and said to him, 'Oh how good a friend is the cook to you, which has given to you so good a bone whereon is so much flesh.'

"The hound said, 'You know nothing thereof. You praise me like as you see me tofore with the bone. But you have not seen me behind. Take heed and behold me afterward on my buttocks and then you shall know how I have deserved it.'

"And when they had seen him behind on his hips how that his skin and his flesh was all raw and through sodden, tho growled them all [248] and were afraid of that seething water and

sodden: boiled

would not of his fellowship, but fled and ran away from him and let him there alone.

"See, my lord, this right [249] have these false beasts when they be made lords and may get their desire and when they be mighty and doubted. Then be they extortioners and scat and pill the people and eat them like as they were forhungered hounds. These be they that bear the bone in their mouth. No man dare have to do with them, but praise all that they bedrive. No man dare say otherwise but such as shall please them because they would not be shorn.[250] And some help them forth in their unrighteous deeds because they would have part and lick their fingers and strengthen them in their evil life and works. Oh dear lord, how little see they that do thus after behind [251] them what the end shall be at the last. They fall from high to low in great shame and sorrow and then their works come to knowledge and be open in such wise that no man has pity or compassion on them in their mischief and trouble. And every man curses them and says evil by them to their shame and villainy. Many of such have been blamed and shorn full nigh that they had no worship nor profit, but lose their hair as the hound did. That is their friends which have helped them to cover their misdeeds and extortions like as the hair covers the skin. And when they have sorrow and shame for their old trespasses, then each body plucks his hand from him and flees like as the hounds did from him that was scalded with the seething water and let him these extortions in their sorrow and need.[252]

"My dear lord king, I beseech you to remember this example of me. It shall not be against your worship nor wisdom. What ween you how many be there such false extortioners now in these days! Yea, much worse than a hound that bears such a

scat: tax   *pill*: rob   *forhungered*: starved

bone in his mouth in towns, in great lords' courts, which with great facing and bracing oppress the poor people with great wrong and sell their freedom and privileges and bear them on hand of [253] things that they never knew nor thought and all to get good for their singular profit. God give them all shame and soon destroy them, whosomever they be that so do.

"But, God be thanked," said the fox, "there may no man indite me nor my lineage nor kin of such works, but that we shall acquit us and come in the light. I am not afraid of any that can say on me anything that I have done otherwise than a true man ought to do. Always the fox shall abide the fox though all his enemies had sworn the contrary. My dear lord the king, I love you with my heart above all lords and never for no man would I turn from you, but abide by you to the utterest, how well it has been otherwise informed your highness. I have, nevertheless, done the best and forth so will do all my life that I can or may."

XLIII. *How the King Forgave the Fox All Things and Made Him Sovereign and Greatest Over All His Lands*

The king said, "Reynard, you be one of them that owes me homage, which I will that you always so do. And also I will that early and late you be of my council and one of my justices. See well to that you not misdo nor trespass no more. I set you again in all your might and power like as you were tofore and see that you further all matters to the best right. For when you set your wit and counsel to virtue and goodness, then may not our court be without your advice and counsel. For here is none that is like to you in sharp and high counsel nor subtler in finding a remedy for a mischief. And think you on the example that you yourself have told and that you haunt right-

facing: boasting   *bracing*: swaggering

eousness and be to me true. I will from henceforth work and do by your advice and counsel. He lives not that if he misdid you, but I should sharply avenge and wreak it on him. You shall overall speak and say my words and in all my lands shall you be above all other sovereign and my bail. That office I give you. You may well occupy it with worship."

All Reynard's friends and lineage thanked the king highly. The king said, "I would do more for your sake than you ween. I pray you all that you remember him that he be true."

Dame Rukenaw then said, "Yes, sikerly, my lord, that shall he ever be. And think you not the contrary; for if he were otherwise, he were not of our kin nor lineage and I would ever missake him and would ever hinder him to my power." 254

Reynard the fox thanked the king with fair courteous words and said, "Dear lord, I am not worthy to have the worship that you do to me. I shall think thereon and be true to you all so long as I live and give you as wholesome counsel as shall be expedient to your grace." Herewith he departed with his friends from the king.

Now hark how Isegrim the wolf did! Bruin the bear, Tibert the cat, and Erswind and her children with their lineage drew the wolf out of the field and laid him upon a litter of hay and covered him warm and looked to his wounds which were well twenty-five. And there came wise masters and surgeons which bound them and washed them. He was so sick and feeble that he had lost his feeling. But they rubbed and wrived him under his temples and eyes that he sprang out of his swoon and cried so loud that all they were afraid. They had weened that he had been wood.

But the masters gave him a drink that comforted his heart and made him to sleep. They comforted his wife and told to

misdid: harmed   *bail*: bailiff   *missake*: renounce
wrived: rubbed

183

her that there was no death wound nor peril of his life. Then the court broke up and the beasts departed and went to their places and homes that they came from.

XLIII. *How the Fox with His Friends and Lineage Departed Nobly from the King and Went to His Castle Maleperduys*

Reynard the fox took his leave honestly of the king and of the queen and they bade him he should not tarry long, but shortly return to them again. He answered and said, "Dear king and queen, always at your commandment I shall be ready if you need anything, which God forbid. I would always be ready with my body and my good to help you and also all my friends and lineage in like wise shall obey your commandment and desire. You have highly deserved it. God quit it you and give you grace long to live! And I desire your license and leave to go home to my wife and children. And if your good grace will anything, let me have knowledge of it and you shall find me always ready." Thus departed the fox with fair words from the king.

Now who that could set him in Reynard's craft and could behave him in flattering and lying as he did, he should I trow be heard both with the lords spiritual and temporal. They be many and also the most part that creep after his way and his hole. The name that was given to him abides always still with him. He has left many of his craft in this world which always wax and become mighty. For who that will not use Reynard's craft now is not worth in the world now in any estate that is of might. But if he can creep into Reynard's net and has been his scholar, then may he dwell with us. For then knows he well the way how he may arise and is set up above of every man. There is in the world much seed left of the fox which now

184

over all grows and comes sore up. Though they have no red beards, yet there be found more foxes now than ever were heretofore. The righteous people be all lost. Truth and righteousness be exiled and fordriven. And for them be abided with us covetise, falsehood, hate, and envy. These reign now much in every country. For is it in the Pope's court, the emperor's, the king's, duke's or any other lord's, wheresomever it be each man labors to put other out from his worship, office, and power for to make himself to climb high with lies, with flattering, with simony, with money, or with strength and force. There is nothing beloved nor known in the court nowadays but money. The money is better beloved than God. For men do much more therefor. For whosomever brings money shall be well received and shall have all his desire, is it of lords or of ladies or of any other. That money does much harm. Money brings many in shame and dread of life and brings false witness against true people for to get money. It causes uncleanness of living, lying, and lechery. Now clerks go to Rome, to Paris, and to many other place for to learn Reynard's craft. Is he clerk, is he layman, every one of them treads in the fox's path and seeks his hole. The world is of such condition now that everyman seeks himself in all matters. I wot not what end shall come to us hereof. All wise men may sorrow well herefor. I fear that for the great falseness, theft, robbery, and murder that is now used so much and commonly and also the unshamefast lechery and avoutry — boasted, blown abroad with the avaunting of the same — that without great repentance and penance therefor that God will take vengeance and punish us sore therefor, whom I humbly beseech and to whom nothing is hid that he will give us grace to make amends therefor and that we may rule us to his pleasure.

unshamefast: shameless   *avaunting*: praising

185

And herewith will I leave, for what have I to write of these misdeeds? I have enough to do with my own self and so it were better that I hold my peace and suffer. And the best that I can, do,[255] for to amend my life now in this time and so I counsel every man to do here in this present life, and that shall be most our profit. For after this life comes no time that we may occupy to our advantage for to amend us. For then shall every man answer for himself and bear his own burden.

Reynard's friends and lineage to the number of forty have taken also their leave of the king and went all together with the fox, which was right glad that he had so well sped and that he stood so well in the king's grace. He thought that he had no shame but that he was so great with the king that he might help and further his friends and hinder his enemies, and also to do what he would, without he should be blamed, if he would be wise.

The fox and his friends went so long together that they came to his burg, to Maleperduys. There they all took leave each of other with fair and courteous words. Reynard did to them great reverence and thanked them all friendly of their good faith and also worship that they had done and showed to him and proffered to each of them his service, if they had need, with body and good. And herewith they departed and each of them went to their own houses.

The fox went to Dame Ermelin his wife, which welcomed him friendly. He told to her and to his children all the wonder that to him was befallen in the court and forgot not a word, but told to them everydeal how he had escaped. Then were they glad that their father was so enhanced and great with the king. And the fox lived forthon with his wife and his children in great joy and gladness.

everydeal: everything

186

boertellken. hi vint daer vele wise leren ende
goede sinnen yn dat hem licht hier na doghet
ende ere in brengen mocht Daer en is nye mãt
goeders ynne beloghen Het is int ghemeyne
voert ghebrocht Elck die treckt hem aen dz
hem toe behoert Soe wie datter verbeteren
kan die maket bet Wie dat syn beste doet die
en is niet te witen Mer die alle dinck berecht=
ten wil die en is gheen dinck te wille te wa=
nen Eñ soe wie dit verscryft die wil dit doch
laten alsoe hyt vyndt

Hier eyndet die hystorie van reynaert
die vos. ende is gheprent ter goude in hollant
by mi gheraert leeu den seuentienden dach in
augusto Int iaer M. CCCC. eñ lxxix
Deo gracias

The colophon of the Gouda edition of 1479

Now who that said to you of the fox more or less than you have heard or read, I hold it for lesing. But this that you have heard or read, that may you believe well. And who that believes it not is not therefore out of the right belief; howbeit there be many, if that they had seen it, they should have the less doubt of it. For there be many things in the world which be believed tho they were never seen. Also there be many figures, plays found, that never were done nor happed. But for an example to the people that they may thereby the better use and follow virtue and to eschew sin and vices, in like wise may it be by this book that who that will read this matter, though it be of japes and bourds, yet he may find therein many a good wisdom and learnings, by which he may come to virtue and worship. There is no good man blamed therein. It is spoken generally. Let every man take his own part as it belongs and behooves and he that finds him guilty in any deal or part thereof, let him better and amend him. And he that is verily good, I pray God keep him therein. And if anything be said or written herein that may grieve or displease any man, blame me not, but the fox. For they be his words and not mine.[256]

Praying all them that shall see this little treatise to correct and amend where they shall find fault, for I have not added nor minished but have followed as nigh as I can my copy, which was in Dutch and by me, William Caxton, translated into this rude and simple English in the Abbey of Westminster; finished the sixth day of June, the year of our Lord 1481 and the twenty-first year of the reign of King Edward the Fourth.

Here ends the history of Reynard the fox, etc.

minished: deleted

BIBLIOGRAPHY

ANNOTATIONS

GLOSSARY

INDEX

ABBREVIATIONS

MLR   *Modern Language Review*

MP   *Modern Philology*

PQ   *Philological Quarterly*

RES   *Review of English Studies*

TLS   *Times Literary Supplement*

BIBLIOGRAPHY

Chapter 1

The Gouda and Caxton Editions

A list of all modern printings of *Reynard* and *Reynaert* together with the more pertinent biographical and bibliographical studies.

Arber, Edward, ed. *The History of Reynard the Fox.* The English Scholar's Library of Old and Modern Works I. London, 1878. An edition with an accurate reproduction of Caxton's 1481 text but without an adequate introduction and without notes and glossary.

Aurner, Nellie S. *Caxton Mirror of Fifteenth Century Letters: A study of the literature of the first English press.* Boston, 1926.

Blades, William. *The Biography and Typography of William Caxton, England's First Printer.* New York, 1882. 2nd ed. The standard work on Caxton originally published 1861–1863 as *The Life and Typography of William Caxton* and again published in a condensed form with alterations and additions in 1877 as *The Biography and Typography of William Caxton.*

Burrell, Arthur, ed. *Reynard the Fox.* London, 19—. An elementary school reader that preserves Caxton's original chapter headings.

Crotch, W. J. B., ed. *The Prologues and Epilogues of William Caxton.* Early English Text Society: Extra Series 176. London, 1928. An edition of all of Caxton's prologues and epilogues introduced by a life of Caxton that brings Blades and Lee up to date.

Ellis, Frederick S. *The History of Reynard the Fox: His friends and his enemies, his crimes, hairbreadth escapes and final triumph.* London, 1897. A metrical version of Caxton's translation.

Goldsmid, Edmund, ed. *The History of Reynard the Fox.* Bibliotheca Curiosa X/XI. Edinburgh, 1884. A copy presumably of Arber's edition with an introduction made up of several paragraphs from Thomas Carlyle's "German Literature of the Fourteenth and Fifteenth Centuries" that appeared in *The Foreign Quarterly Review* of July and October 1831, vol. VIII, no. xvi.

Jacobs, Joseph, ed. *The Most Delectable History of Reynard the Fox.* London, 1895. A version that follows Felix Summerly's edition of Caxton's *Reynard* for children.

Kronenberg, Maria. "Gheraert Leeu." *Nieuw Nederlandsch Biogra-*

BIBLIOGRAPHY

fisch Woordenboek. Leiden, 1924. VI, 918–921. A biography provided with full documentation.

Lee, Sidney. "Caxton." *The Dictionary of National Biography*.

Mish, Charles C. "*Reynard the Fox* in the Seventeenth Century." *Huntington Library Quarterly*, XVII, 4 (August 1954), 327–344. A significant article that relates how the 1550 printing, actually the 5th edition of Caxton's *Reynard*, served as the basis for a complete reworking of the story which, in its many mutations, held the field until well into the 19th century when Thoms's edition for the Percy Society again brought Caxton's translation to the press after almost three hundred years.

Morley, Henry, ed. "The History of Reynard the Fox." *Early Prose Romances*. The Carisbrooke Library IV. London, 1889. pp. 43–166. A rather close copy of Caxton, probably from Arber's edition, with modern paragraphing, punctuation, orthography.

Morris, William, ed. *The History of Reynard the Fox*. Hammersmith, 1892. A deluxe reprint of Caxton provided with a fifteenth century colophon.

Muller, Jacob W. and Henri Logeman, edd. *Die Hystorie van Reynaert die Vos naar den druk van 1479 vergeleken met William Caxton Engelsche Vertaling*. Zwolle, 1892. The only scholarly edition of the Gouda book; see Hellinga in the Bibliography of Chapter II for a diplomatic reprint.

Owens, Harry J., ed. *The Scandalous Adventures of Reynard the Fox: A modern version*. New York, 1945. A highly colloquial retelling of the basic Caxton version.

de Ricci, Seymour. *A Census of Caxtons*. Illustrated Monographs of the Bibliographic Society XV. Oxford, 1909. A standard work describing individual editions and listing their location.

Smyth, Charlotte S., ed. *Reynard the Fox*. New York, 1931. A child's version of *Reynard* that holds to the Caxton version throughout.

Stallybrass, William S., ed. *The Epic of the Beast: Consisting of English translations of the History of Reynard the Fox and Physiologus*. With an introduction by William Rose. Broadway Translations. London, 1924. pp. v–xxxviii, 1–151. A modernized version of Caxton's text with an introduction that almost overlooks Caxton and treats the Flemish epics only briefly.

Suhl, Ludwig, ed. *Die Historie van Reynaert de Vos: Nach der Delfter Ausgabe von 1485 zum genauen Abdrucke befördert*. Lübeck, 1783. The only modern reprint of the Delft edition.

Summerly, Felix, ed. *The Pleasant History of Reynard the Fox Told*

192

by the Pictures of Aldert van Everdingen. London, 1843. A retelling of Caxton for children.

Thoms, William J., ed. *The History of Reynard the Fox.* Percy Society XII. London, 1844. The edition that began the 19th century reprints of Caxton's original text.

—— "The History of Reynard the Fox." *Early English Prose Romances.* Introduction by Henry Morley. London, 1907. pp. 43–166. A reprint of the Morley text.

Chapter II

The Rise of Reynard in the Low Countries

Major editions and translations of Continental beast epics

Baesecke, Georg, ed. *Das älteste deutsche Tierepos aus der Sprache des 12. Jahrhunderts in unsere Übertragung.* Halle, 1926.

Bieling, Alexander, ed. *Reineke Fuchs: Abdruck der hochdeutschen Prosa-Übersetzung vom Jahre 1752.* Quellenschriften zur neueren deutschen Literatur Nr 1. Halle, 1886. A reprint of Gottsched's prose translation.

Boon, Louis P., trans. *Wapenbroeders: Een getrouwe bewerking der aloude boeken over Reinaert en Isengrimus.* Amsterdam, 1955. A modern Dutch retelling of the adventures of Reynard and Isegrim using *Ysengrimus*, *Reinaert I*, and the *Roman de Renart.*

Breul, Karl, ed. *The Cambridge Reinaert Fragments (Culemann Fragments).* Cambridge, 1927.

Campbell, M. F. A. G., ed. *Reynardus Vulpes.* The Hague, 1859.

Chauveau, Leopold, trans. *Le Roman de Renard.* Paris, 1924. A modern French retelling of the *Roman.*

Dijkstra, R., ed. *Reinaert: Oudste text vor een ieder verstaanbaar gemaakt door interlineaire vertaling van de verouderde woorden en uitdrukkingen.* Rotterdam, 1883.

Gottsched, Johann Christoph, trans. *Henrichs van Alkmar Reineke der Fuchs mit schönen Kupfern, nach der Ausgabe von 1498 ins Hochdeutsche übersetzt.* Leipzig, 1752. The modern German prose translation of *Reinke de Vos* of 1498 that inspired Goethe to write out Reynard's story in hexameters and that in its title ascribes *Reinke* incorrectly to the man who probably edited *Reinaert II* for its 1487 printing in Antwerp, 222 lines of which survive today as the "Cambridge Fragments."

Gräter, F. D., ed. *Van den Vos Reynaerde: Die erste entdeckte Handschrift des Reineke Fuchs in flammändischer Sprache.* Bragur Bd

193

8. Leipzig, 1812. The first printing of *Reinaert I* in modern times.
Grimm, Jacob, ed. *Reinhart Fuchs*. Berlin, 1834. A medley of Reynard
texts including *Reinaert I* and part of *Reinaert II* and the work
whose introduction marks the beginning of modern beast epic
scholarship.
Hellinga, Wytze Gs, ed. *Van den Vos Reynaerde. I Teksten: Diplo-
matisch uitgegeven naar de bronnen voor het jaar 1500*. Zwolle,
1952. A work that contains all the Middle Dutch epics, prose as
well as verse, plus the Latin *Reinardus Vulpes*, all printed in
parallel order.
Hettema, Buitenrust and J. W. Muller, eds. *Van den Vos Reynaerde:
Opnieuw naar het Comburgesche Handschrift Uitgegeven met
inleiding, aanteekeningen en woordenlijst*. Zwolsche Herdrukken
XVIII–XX. Zwolle, 1903–1909.
Jonckbloet, Joseph A., ed. *Van den Vos Reinaerde*. Groningen, 1856.
de Keyser, Paul, ed. *Reinaerts Historie: HS Koninklijke Bibliotheek
14601*. Werken uitgegeven door de Faculteit van de Wijsbegeerte
en Letteren, Extra Serie: Facsimiles I. Rijksuniversiteit to Gent.
Antwerp, 1938. A photographic reproduction with introduction
and bibliography of the one complete *Reinaert II* manuscript.
Knorr, Wilhelm, ed. *Reinardus Vulpes*. Eutin, 1860.
Leitzmann, Albert, ed. *Reinke de Vos*. Paul-Baesecke's Altdeutsche
Textbibliothek VIII. Halle, 1925. The best edition of the 1498
Lübeck adaptation of Henric van Alcmaer's verse *Reinaert* sur-
viving only in the "Cambridge Fragments" with an introduction
by Karl Voretzsch, the sanest of German Reynard historians.
Martin, Ernst, ed. *Reinaert: Willems Gedicht van den Vos Reinaerde
und die Umarbeitung und Fortsetzung Reinaerts Historie*. Pader-
born, 1874. The best edition for the student of both *Reinaert I* and
Reinaert II with introduction, notes, a Middle Dutch grammar,
and glossary.
────── *Le Roman de Renart*. Strassburg, 1882. 3 vols. *Supplement*.
Strassburg, 1887. The standard work.
van Mierlo, Jan, trans. *Magister Nivardus' Isengrimus*. Antwerp, 1946.
A modern Flemish translation into alexandrines, not as close to
the original Latin text as is the German translation by Schönfelder.
Méon, M. D. M., ed. *Le Roman de Renart*. Paris, 1826. 4 vols. *Supplement*. P. Chabaille, ed. Paris, 1835. The first work to attempt to
gather together Renart versions.
Mone, Franz J., ed. *Reinardus Vulpes*. Stuttgart, 1832. The first edition of *Ysengrimus* that uses the title now applied to the Latin
translation of *Reinaert I*.

CAXTON'S DISCOVERY OF REYNARD

Muller, Jacob W., ed. *Van den Vos Reinaerde*. Leidsche Drukken en Herdrukken uitgegeven vanwege de Maatschappij der Nederlandsche Letterkunde to Leiden: Groote Reeks I & II. Leiden, 1939–1942. The two volume edition of *Reinaert I* that contains Muller's final theories.

Poll, Max, trans. *Van den Vos Reynaerde*. University of Cincinnati Studies VIII. Cincinnati, 1914. A translation of *Reinaert I* into modern German prose.

Roques, Mario, ed. *Le Roman de Renart*. Les classiques français du moyen âge 78, 79, 81. Paris, 1948–1955. An up-to-date editing of the *Roman* that supersedes Martin's edition.

Schönfelder, Albert, trans. *Isengrimus: Das flämische Tierepos aus dem Lateinischen verdeutscht*. Niederdeutsche Studien herausgegeben von William Foerste Bd III. Münster/Köln, 1955. A modern German translation with introduction and notes.

Schröbler, Ingeborg, ed. *Das mittelhochdeutsche Gedicht vom Fuchs Reinhart nach den Casseler Bruckstücken und der Heidelberger Hs Cod. pal. germ. 341*. Altdeutsche Textbibliothek Nr 7. Halle, 1952. The standard edition that is actually the second edition of Georg Baesecke's *Heinrich des Glichezares Reinhart Fuchs* of 1925 but without Karl Voretzsch's excellent introduction.

Tinbergen, D. C., ed. *Van den Vos Reinaerde*. Van alle Tijden. Bibliotheek van Nederlandse letterkunde onder redactie van Dr. L. M. van Dis. Groningen, 1956. 14th ed. by L. M. van Dis. The handiest of all modern edited texts of *Reinaert I*.

Voigt, Ernst, ed. *Ysengrimus*. Halle, 1884.

Willems, Jan-Frans, ed. *Reinaert de Vos: Episch fabeldicht van de twaelfde en dertiende eeuw met aenmerkingen en ophelderingen*. Ghent, 1836. The first attempt by a modern scholar to edit *Reinaert I* and *Reinaert II* in one volume.

Chapter III

William Caxton's Discovery of Reynard the Fox

The major factually reliable works treating Caxton's life story are listed in the bibliography for Chapter I. There are, to be sure, several long eighteenth and nineteenth century biographies of Caxton, but these have been rendered obsolete by the works of Aurner, Blades, Crotch, and Lee, although scholars of Caxton scholarship should be familiar with biographers like Ames, Dibdin, Herbert, Knight, and Lewis, who, despite their appearance in modern bibliographies, wrote

195

much that we must now reject as hearsay. The following bibliography, which is designed to be as complete as possible, lists studies that throw light on Caxton as a literary figure. Presumably, each entry cites a work that is readily available in a large library and that makes a genuine contribution to our understanding of Caxton's literary personality. Omitted are purely typographic and bibliographic studies; standard histories of English literature; a myriad of nineteenth century articles, chiefly belletristic appreciations that appeared in such journals as *Antiquary, Athenaeum, Book-Lore, Bookworm, Leisure Hour, Literary World, Penny Magazine, Practical Magazine,* and the London *Saturday Review*; and finally, edited editions of Caxton's translations. Concerning these last, and considerations of space are responsible for their omission, especial note should be taken of the Early English Text Society publications, which in their introductions offer material, if not always on Caxton himself, then certainly on the literature of his age. A selective, up-to-date bibliography of the general phases of Caxton study will appear in the near future with the publication of the first volume of the revision of John Edwin Wells's *A Manual of the Writings in Middle English.*

Aurner, Robert R. "Caxton and the English Sentence." *Wisconsin Studies in Language and Literature,* Series 3, XVIII. Madison, 1923. pp. 23–59. A clear description of Caxton's syntax followed by a brief evaluation of his prose.
Bennett, Henry S. "The Author and His Public in the Fourteenth and Fifteenth Centuries." *Essays and Studies of the English Association* XXIII, collected by S. C. Roberts. Oxford and London, 1938. pp. 7–24. An account of what patronage meant to authors up to and during Caxton's day.
——— "Caxton and His Public." *RES,* XIX.74 (April 1943), 113–119. An argument that interest in vernacular writings of all kinds before and during Caxton's day explains Caxton's catholicity of subject matter.
——— *Chaucer and the Fifteenth Century.* Oxford, 1947.
——— *English Books and Readers 1475 to 1557: Being a study in the history of the book trade from Caxton to the incorporation of the Stationer's Company.* Cambridge, Eng., 1952.
——— "Fifteenth-Century Secular Prose." *RES,* XXI.84 (October 1945), 257–263. An essay pointing out the simplicity and clarity of which 15th century prose was capable.
——— "Science and Information in English Writings of the Fifteenth Century." *MLR,* XXXIX.1 (January 1944), 1–8. A summary of

the wide variety of chiefly informational works during Caxton's day.

Bennett, J. A. W. "Caxton and Gower." *MLR*, XLV.2 (April 1950), 215–216. A note on Caxton's use of material by Gower for his own translation from the French of Ovid's *Metamorphoses*.

Binns, Norman E. *Introduction to Historical Bibliography*. London, 1953. pp. 111–129.

Blades, Rowland H. "Who Was Caxton?" *The Library*, 2nd Series, IV.14 (April 1903), 113–143. A well-rounded sketch of Caxton's life by the brother of the great William Blades.

ten Brink, Bernhard. *Geschichte der englischen Literatur*. 2nd ed., vol. II, part II. Strassburg, 1912.

Byles, A. T. P. "William Caxton as a Man of Letters." *The Library*, 4th Series, XVI.1 (June 1934), 1–25. An informal essay on the problem of Caxton's prose style, resolved with much credit being given to Caxton's prose abilities.

"Caxton and His Public." *TLS*, Sept. 4, 1943. An account that regrets the tendency apparently initiated by Lathrop and carried on by H. S. Bennett of imputing a lack of originality and critical perception to Caxton as an editor.

Colvile, K. N. "William Caxton: Man of Letters." *The Quarterly Review*, CCXLVIII.491 (January 1927), 165–178. An appreciation that contains a useful breakdown of Caxton's works into their respective categories, but in so doing does not admit that Caxton learned the art of printing in Cologne.

Crotch, W. J. B. "Caxton Documents." *The Library*, 4th Series, VIII.4 (March 1928), 426–455. A list of documents supplementing those in the 1861 *Life* of Caxton by William Blades, omitted in the 1882 edition.

——— "Caxton on the Continent." *The Library*, 4th Series, VII.4 (March 1927), 387–401.

——— "Caxton's Son-in-law." *The Library*, 4th Series, IX.1 (June 1928), 48–52.

——— "An Englishman of the Fifteenth Century." *Economica*, X.28 (March 1930), 56–73. A readable account of Caxton's career as a merchant and ambassador in the Low Countries.

Deanesly, Margaret. "Vernacular Books in England in the Fourteenth and Fifteenth Centuries." *MLR*, XV.4 (October 1920), 349–358. A listing of books bequeathed in medieval wills that gives a picture of the reading habits of Englishmen before and during Caxton's day.

Duff, Edward G. *A Century of the English Book Trade.* London: The Bibliographical Society, 1905.
—— *The Printers, Stationers, and Bookbinders of Westminster and London from 1476 to 1535.* Cambridge, 1906. pp. 1–23. A general coverage of Caxton's career with more emphasis on his character and ideas than in the usual biographical treatment.
—— *William Caxton.* Chicago, 1905.
Faltenbacher, Hans. *Die romanischen, speziell französischen und lateinischen (bzw. latinisierten) Lehnwörter bei Caxton.* Munich, 1907.
Flügel, Ewald. "Caxton's Old English Words." *MP*, I.2 (October 1903), 343.
Hammerschlag, Johannes. *Dialekteinflüsse im frühneuenglischen Wortschatz, nachgewiesen an Caxton und Fabyan.* Bonner Studien zur englischen Philologie, Heft 31. Bonn, 1937. A treatment of occasional Northern and Kentish forms in Caxton's prose.
Hittmair, Rudolf. *William Caxton, Englands erster Drucker und Verleger.* Innsbruck, 1931.
Housman, John E. "Higden, Trevisa, Caxton, and the Beginnings of Arthurian Criticism." *RES*, XXIII.91 (July 1947), 209–217. An account of Caxton's skepticism regarding the historicity of King Arthur.
Lathrop, Henry B. "The First English Printers and Their Patrons." *The Library*, 4th Series, III.2 (September 1922), 69–96. An evaluation of Caxton that assigns his literary energies chiefly to self-interest.
Leisi, Ernst. *Die tautologischen Wortpaare in Caxton's 'Eneydos':* *Zur synchronischen Bedeutungs- und Ursachenforschung.* New York, 1947.
Mossé, Fernand. "Le Roman de Renart dans l'Angleterre du moyen âge." *Les langues modernes*, XLV.2 (Mars-Avril 1951), 22–36. An excellent coverage of the Latin fabulists who treated fox and wolf fables in England before the time of Chaucer.
"New Caxton Records." *TLS*, April 5, 1923. A report of Birch's discovery of entries in the register of aliens at Cologne for the years 1471–1472 that indicates that Caxton resided there.
Pirkhofer, Anton. "Zum syntaktischen Gebrauch des bestimmten Artikels bei Caxton." *Englische Studien*, LXX.1 (January 1935), 92–101.
Plomer, Henry R. *A Short History of English Printing 1476–1900.* New York, 1927. 2nd ed. pp. 1–26.
—— *William Caxton 1424–1491.* London, 1925.

Pollard, Alfred W. *Early Illustrated Books: A history of the decoration and illustration of books in the 15th and 16th centuries.* London, 1893. pp. 223–249.

———— *Fifteenth Century Prose and Verse.* New York, 1903. pp. 211–242.

———— "The New Caxton Indulgence." *The Library,* 4th Series, IX.1 (June 1928), 86–89. The description of an indulgence that indicates Caxton was printing in England by December 1476.

———— "William Caxton's Stay at Cologne." *The Library,* 4th Series, IV.1 (June 1923), 50–52. A more scholarly account of the evidence that Caxton resided in Cologne than that given in "New Caxton Records" above.

de Reul, Paul. *The Language of Caxton's Reynard the Fox: A study in historical English syntax.* Ghent, 1901. The handiest grammar of Caxton's language.

Roberts, W. Wright. "William Caxton, Writer and Critic." *Bulletin of the John Rylands Library,* XIV.2 (July 1930), 410–422. An account of Caxton's "Tudor dialect" and his significance in the development of English literary criticism.

Römstedt, Hermann. *Die englische Schriftsprache bei Caxton.* Preisschrift. Göttingen, 1891.

Sands, Donald B. "William Blades' Comment on Caxton's 'Reynard the Fox': The genealogy of an error." *Notes and Queries,* NS I.2 (February 1954), 50–51. A note that points out that Blades was relying on evidence he had not actually seen when he suggested that there might be a source for Caxton's *Reynard* other than the Gouda edition.

———— "William Caxton as a Literary Critic." *Papers of the Bibliographical Society of America,* 51, 4th quarter (October 1957), 312–318. An analysis of all of Caxton's publications that shows he recognized enduring literature and published it when he could.

Shackford, Martha H. *Caxton's Esope: Renaissance Landmark.* Natick, Mass., 1953.

Sheppard, Leslie A. "A New Light on Caxton and Colard Mansion." *Signature,* NS XV (1952), 28–39. A significant article that advances the theory that Caxton taught Colard Mansion how to print; an excellent evaluation of the implications of this article by Curt F. Bühler, *The Library,* 5th Series, VIII.1 (March 1953), 53–56.

Tanner, Lawrence E. "William Caxton's Houses at Westminster." *The Library,* 5th Series, XII.3 (September 1957), 153–166. An analysis that theorizes Caxton's shop at the Red Pale was somehow connected with Westminster Abbey.

Thomas, Henry. *Wilh. Caxton uyss Engelant: Evidence that the first English printer learned his trade at Cologne.* London, 1928.

Wiencke, Helmut. *Die Sprache Caxtons.* Kölner anglistische Arbeiten XI. Leipzig, 1930. A study of Caxton's language that in its phonological aspects is particularly rewarding.

Wilson, Richard H. "The Poggiana in Caxton's 'Esope.' " *PQ*, XXX.3 (July 1951), 348–352. An investigation of how much in the fables of Poggio inserted at the end of Caxton's *Esope* are actually of Caxton's authorship.

Wilson, Richard M. *The Lost Literature of Medieval England.* London, 1952.

Winkler, Gerda. *Das Relativum bei Caxton und seine Entwicklung von Chaucer bis Spenser.* Inaugural Diss. Saalfeld, 1933. A detailed treatment of Caxton's relative constructions.

Winship, George P. *William Caxton and His Work.* Berkeley, 1937.

Workman, Samuel K. *Fifteenth Century Translation as an Influence on English Prose.* Princeton and London, 1940.

ANNOTATIONS

(A superscript asterisk * placed before a word indicates that the word is not found in written documents and that it has been construed by analogy with other similar words which do have recorded forms.)

1. *Pentecost or Whitsuntide.* The seventh Sunday after Easter when the secular activities of the medieval courts of law began.

2. *Stade.* A place name Caxton thought he saw in the Gouda *te stade*, which translates *mit groten love* of *Reinaert II*, both phrases meaning "with great ceremony." Caxton, however, may have had one of two Low German towns of this name in mind: one on the Schwinge between Hamburg and Cuxhaven and the other in West Flanders to the north of Ypres.

3. *Did to know.* Caused to be made known.

4. *Reynard.* A Germanic name made up of two elements originally meaning "very" and "hard." The name *Reynard* exists in modern Dutch as *Reintje* and in modern German as *Reineke* as a byname for a fox; it exists in modern French as *renard*, a word which has replaced the native *goupil* as the word for fox; and it exists in modern German as the man's name *Reinhard*. The modern English *Reynard* preserves the Middle Dutch form *Reynaert* introduced by Caxton. *Reynard* as a byname in English for fox was foreshadowed by Chaucer's use of *Russel* in "The Nun's Priest's Tale," although the name in Chaucer is via Old French related to *Rosseel*, one of Reynard's sons in the Middle Dutch epics.

5. *Isegrim.* A Germanic name made up of two elements originally meaning "iron" and "mask."

6. *As he nought set thereby.* As though he placed little importance thereto.

7. *Curtois.* A name of Old French origin meaning "courteous" and applied here to a lap dog and in late Middle Dutch literature to a libertine or dandy.

8. *Forwintered.* The implication is that his provisions had been sorely depleted by the very severe winter.

9. *Tibert.* A Germanic name, originally * *Theodoberht* and one which appears in *Romeo and Juliet* (II, iv, 18) in a pun on "Tibalt."

10. *Cuwart.* A name, related to English "coward," itself of Old French origin, and ultimately related to Latin *cauda* (tail), implying

an animal that either "turns tail" or runs with its tail between its legs.

11. *Grimbert.* A Germanic name made up of two elements originally meaning "mask" and "bright."

12. *Dasse.* Caxton's word has again appeared in English from Afrikaans in the form *das,* meaning "rock badger."

13. *Sisterson.* The relationship between a man and his sister's son was in early Germanic times traditionally close. This relationship is noted in Tacitus's *Germania* (chap. X) and is evidenced throughout medieval literature, Gawain being Arthur's sisterson, Beowulf Hygelac's, and Roland Charlemagne's.

14. *But and if . . . ask him forgiveness.* In both Caxton and the Gouda edition a confused sentence. *Reinaert II* is clear: "But were he [Reynard] so well at court and stood he so well in the king's esteem, Sir Isegrim, as you, then it shouldn't seem good to him if you remained unpunished for this [open accusation]."

15. *Vysevase.* A word Caxton took directly from the Gouda edition, perhaps uncertain of its meaning; the Middle Dutch word, usually *visevase,* here means "senseless talk" and exists in modern Dutch as *viezevaas.*

16. *Mainour.* From Old French *maneuvre* (handwork), but now in legal usage in the phrase "with" or "in the mainour" meaning "in the act of doing something unlawful."

17. *Maleperduys.* So in the Gouda edition, but *Maupertuus* in *Reinaert I* and *Malpertuis* in the *Roman* and made up from Old French *mal* (evil) and *pertuis* (hole).

18. *Grimbert, his eme.* A blunder on Caxton's part; Reynard is Grimbert's uncle. Caxton translated the *van sinen oem* (concerning his uncle) of the Gouda edition as an appositive.

19. *Chanticleer.* In the Gouda edition *cantenkleer,* a form indicating derivation from northern Old French, whereas Caxton's form and Chaucer's *Chauntecleer* indicate origin in central Old French, Caxton, no doubt, here echoing Chaucer rather than the prose editor of the Gouda edition.

20. *Cantart.* A name of Old French origin related to modern French *chanter* (to sing).

21. *Crayant.* A name not appearing in the *Roman,* derived from Middle Dutch *craeyen* (to crow), related to modern English "crow," and ending in the Old French suffix *-ant.*

22. *Coppen.* A hen who appears, also dead, in the *Roman* as *Couppee,* who, unlike other fowl in the section, does not have a name that indicates vocal attributes, and whose name is closer perhaps to a Mid-

dle Dutch word *cop* (rounded protrusion) than to a word ultimately related to Latin *cupa* (tub).

23. *Smoked*. In the Gouda edition *dat hem sinen pels stoef* (so that [hair] flew like dust from his hide), but the English idiom means "so that vapor rose from his hide [under the beating]" and is used transitively in Shakespeare, *King John*, II, 1, 139.

24. *Slavin and pilch*. The former was specifically a pilgrim's garment, but the latter can only be identified now as an outer garment of skin dressed with the hair or later of leather or coarse wool.

25. *Forthon*. Here not meaning "therefore," but rather "henceforth," which translates the *voert an* of the Gouda edition.

26. *Sext, none*. Offices recited at the sixth and ninth canonical hours.

27. *Forslongen*. A nonce word in English translating *verslongen* (gobbled up) of the Gouda edition which Caxton modified by changing the Middle Dutch suffix *ver-* to English *for-* (to pieces).

28. *Placebo Domino*. The vespers for the Dead, the first antiphon of which is *Placebo Domino*.

29. *Bruin*. A name derived from a common Germanic adjective meaning "brown" and present also in the *Roman* as *Brun* and retained in English as a byname for a bear in the Middle Dutch form introduced by Caxton.

30. *Casus*. The reference is to the cases of nouns in the Latin declension, the learning of which was the first step in medieval instruction in grammar.

31. *Browning*. A translation of *brunink* of the Gouda edition, used once by Caxton and once in the Gouda edition.

32. *Rat*. Caxton's word is the Middle Dutch word *rat*, a contrivance in the form of a wheel on which criminals were executed and later exposed.

33. *Red*. The adjective here harks back perhaps to a meaning "false." See Robert Sprenger, "Zu Reinke Vos," *Germania Vierteljahrschrift für deutsche Altertumskunde*, XXI, ix, 3 (1876), 350–351.

34. *Lantfert*. A name, appearing in the *Roman* as *Lanfroi*, of Germanic origin made up of two elements originally meaning "land" and "peace" and represented in its early Middle Dutch form as *Lamfreit*.

35. *Hamber*. A liquid measure. The original English *amber* was not used in English after 1100, but Caxton's *hamber*, taken from Middle Dutch *aemen* of the Gouda edition and meaning "vat," harks back to it.

36. *Yonst*. A nonce word that appears in the Gouda edition as *gunsten* and which Caxton, unsure as to its actual use in England of 1481, glossed as "good will" in context.

37. *Crutched.* A word which may be a misprint on Caxton's part for the preterite of *cratch* (to scratch) and which is equivalent to *crassede* (scraped) of the Gouda edition.

38. *Hedge.* Translates *tuyn-* of the Gouda edition's *tuynstake* (fence post).

39. *Priest's wife.* So in *Reinaert I, des papen wijf,* which was written at a time when sacerdotal celibacy, advanced *inter alia* by Pope Innocence III, 1198–1216, was being promulgated.

40. *Julock.* A woman's name common in medieval Zeeland and with the diminutive or endearing Middle Dutch suffix *-ok,* as seen in other Middle Dutch names, as *Eynoc, Hobuc,* and *Madoc.*

41. *She sat tho and spun.* An awkward translation of the Gouda edition's *daer si omme hadde sitten spinnen* (at which she had been sitting to spin).

42. *Market.* In the Gouda edition *vaert* (journey). Caxton's *market* may have here the commercial ring of "business venture."

43. *Hughelin.* A man's name from Middle Dutch *Hughe,* related to modern German *Hugo,* with the diminutive suffix *-lin.*

44. *Ludolf.* A man's name deriving from Germanic and made up of two elements originally meaning "folk" and "wolf."

45. *Wapper.* A nonce word in English translating *wappere* "a leather strap or cudgel loaded or weighted with lead" of the Gouda edition.

46. *Forslingered.* A nonce word in English translating *slingeren* (to beat) of the Gouda edition to which Caxton added the native English suffix *for-* (to pieces).

47. *Bertolt.* A man's name deriving from Germanic and probably existing once in the form * *Berht-wald.*

48. *Ottram.* A man's name deriving from Germanic and probably existing once in the form * *Ald-hram.*

49. *Baetkin.* A person's name found only in the Caxton and Gouda versions of Reynard and made up apparently of the Middle Dutch *bate* (help) plus the diminutive suffix *-kin.*

50. *Ave.* A woman's name in *Reinaert II,* where the phrase *Ave soete* (sweet Ave) appears, and also in Robert Manning's story of the sacrilegious carollers.

51. *Abelquak.* A name made up of the Middle Dutch forms *abel* (clever) and *quacken* (to talk nonsense) and implying to a Middle Dutch audience "flatterer" or "coaxer."

52. *Bave.* A woman's name of Germanic origin from a basic form *Bava,* feminine of *Bavo,* and common in medieval Flanders.

53. *Pogge of Chafport.* A name, possibly with a double meaning in

the Middle Dutch form *Pogge van cafpoerten, Pogge* meaning "toad" or "young pig" and *caf-* (chaff) and *-poerten* (port).

54. *Macob the stopple maker.* In the Gouda edition *Macop ende stoppelmader* (Macop and stubble mower); in Caxton Macob is a "cork" or "bung maker."

55. *Best of the stream.* That is, "toward the main current."

56. *Chiere preistre, dieu vous garde.* In the Gouda edition *Chyre priester dieux vos faut,* which Caxton amended.

57. *Dier.* Taken without change from the Gouda edition.

58. *Compline.* The last service of the day in Catholic ritual.

59. *There lies not on.* A translation of the Gouda edition's *daer en ligt niet an* (there is no concern) and probably not idiomatic in English even in Caxton's day.

60. *Saint Martin's birds.* Not necessarily a goose, but what bird is meant is not certain. The idea behind Tibert's thoughts is common in folklore.

61. *Reyner.* So printed here and perhaps an intentionally shortened form.

62. *Reyner, quod the fox.* Caxton's oversight. *Fox* here should read *cat.*

63. *Montpelier.* A city in Southern France famous in the Middle Ages for the faculties of law and medicine of its university.

64. *Ystrangled.* The past participial prefix *y-* is rarely used in *Reynard.*

65. *Martinet.* A common name both in Flanders and France during the Middle Ages and made up of Martin plus the diminutive *-et.*

66. *In an evil time.* In an unlucky hour.

67. *Locken.* A clipped form of *Julock* and probably a pet name.

68. *Third time.* Correct legal procedure, at least in the time of *Reinaert I,* but later perhaps part of the mock courtly atmosphere of the story.

69. *Ermelin.* A name which is simply one of the Middle Dutch forms of the word for "ermine."

70. *There be greater adventures fallen ere this.* As much as, "Greater chances have been taken before this."

71. *Reynkin.* A name made up of Reynard's first syllable plus the Middle Dutch diminutive *-kin* and close to the form for the fox's byname common in Modern Dutch.

72. *Rossel.* A name, ultimately related to Old French *roux/rousse* (red brown) and cognate to *Russel,* the name of the colfox in Chaucer's "Nun's Priest's Tale."

73. *He that sorrowed.* A translation of the Gouda edition's *be-*

ANNOTATIONS

sorgher, a word etymologically cognate to English *sorrow*, but in the present sense unhistorical in English.

74. *Confiteor tibi pater.* Caxton, perhaps punctiliously, changed the slightly irreverent original, which reads *Confiteor tibi, pater, mater*.

75. *English.* The Gouda edition reads *duytsche.*

76. *Her.* Caxton changes the cat's sex.

77. *Elmare.* A Benedictine priory between Aardenburg and Biervliet destroyed by inundation in 1424.

78. *Vermedos.* The ancient French province of Vermandois in East Picardy, linked by the marriage of its rulers to Flanders 1156–1186.

79. *Erswind.* A name derived ultimately from an old Germanic form often listed as *Heriswintha*, but in *Reinaert II*, the Gouda edition, and Caxton undoubtedly used with a double meaning.

80. *Might not out of.* Might not depart from.

81. *Noble.* A name of Romance origin ultimately related to Latin *nobilis*.

82. *In nomine Pater Christe Filii.* Probably intentionally incorrect, the usual sequence being *In nomine patriis et filii et spiritus sancti.*

83. *Bellin.* A name now thought to be derived not from Old French *beeler*, itself from Latin *balare* (to bleat), but from a form of the original Dutch *bel-* in *belhamel* (bellwether) that Old French formed into the *Belin* of the *Roman* and that was later borrowed back into Middle Dutch.

84. *Olewey.* A name developed from *Hawi* of *Reinaert I*, itself from Old French *Haouis*, derived ultimately from an old German form resembling * *Hadu-wih.*

85. *Brunel.* A name used traditionally as that of the ass (as in Chaucer's "Nun's Priest's Tale"), but here as that of the goose, the name *Boudewin* being given the ass, and derived from an Old Germanic adjective meaning "brown."

86. *Boudewin.* A name, familiar in its form *Baldwin*, of Germanic origin derived from two elements that once meant "bold" and "friend." See note on *Brunel* above.

87. *Borre.* In *Reinaert II* as *Borrell*, but absent in *Reinaert I*. A name that all glosses seem to ignore; in Middle Dutch there are several words of similar appearance: *bore* (drill), *bore* (braid), *boreel* (twist of hair), and *borre*, a form of *borne* (spring).

88. *Hamel.* A name that appears in the Gouda edition as the word *harmel* (ermine); Caxton mistook the word for Middle Dutch *hamel* (wether), made it into an animal's byname, and then added the incorrect species name "ox."

89. *Pertilot.* Not in the Gouda edition nor *Reinaerts I* or *II*; Cax-

ton's addition and an indication that he here recalls Chaucer's "Nun's Priest's Tale."

90. *Balked.* Probably "bellowed," which is the sense of the Gouda edition's *ballech*, preterite of *belken / belleken.*

91. *If I dared I would pay you of mercy.* Caxton's rendering of *dorst ic ick woude v ghenade doen* (if I dared, I would show you mercy) in the Gouda edition; the statement is ironic.

92. *As far as they would come to the gallows.* A puzzling clause wherein various antecedents for *they*, as "the king and his men" or "Bruin and Isegrim," and various senses for *would come*, as "would like to go" or "shall go," can be posed, but without much help. The Gouda edition is simply *nv quamen si daer die galghe stont* (now they came to where the gallows stood).

93. *I might over.* I might overcome.

94. *Scat.* Here in the Middle Dutch sense "treasure" and not "tax," this latter being the sense of Middle English *scat* derived from Old Norse *skattr.*

95. *In eschewing of more harm.* In order that he [the king] might avoid further harm. The fact that no actual harm was ever present from the "feat" referred to by Reynard is the irony intended — here, in the Gouda edition, and in *Reinaerts I* and *II.*

96. *King Ermerik.* The Ermanrik of heroic legend, associated with the Low Countries in that it was believed he built a fortress at Ghent.

97. *Ifte.* Hifte in *Reinaert I,* a town in the Middle Ages, now a hamlet, northeast of Ghent between Loochristi and Desteldonk.

98. *Sworc on Bruin's crown.* Bruin's *crown* (clerical tonsure) takes the place of the relics upon which oaths were often sworn.

99. *Slopecade.* A name found in this form only in the Gouda and Caxton editions and probably in its original Middle Dutch form meaning "drag fat" or "slip in the dike."

100. *Holy three kings of Cologne.* That is, Gaspar, Melchior, and Balthasar. Rainald von Dassel brought their relics from Milan to Cologne in 1164. The *Reinaert II* poet added mention of them to *Reinaert I* and Caxton added "of Cologne" to the Gouda text, an indication that he was at least familiar with the repute of the city where in 1471 he is supposed to have learned to print.

101. *Bedwongen.* The result of an awkward translation. The Gouda text reads *ende claechden dat hoerre to vele onbedwonghen waren* (and complained that too many of them were without constraint).

102. *To strength their king.* The power of their king.

103. *Can me but little thank.* Show me but little thanks.

104. *Elbe and the Somme.* The area bracketed by the two rivers

207

accurately demarcates the area in which the Renart-Reinaert-Reinke literature arose.

105. *Saxony.* The area meant here would be Lower Saxony in North Germany and the East Netherlands.

106. *Abode . . . after.* Came to nought.

107. *Bouche.* Probably a misprint for *benche* (bench), which stands in the Gouda edition as *banc*.

108. *Ninth degree.* That is, the ninth step in direct line of descent.

109. *Straw.* Ludicrous as it may seem, the handing over of a straw as a symbol of departure or renunciation was, even at the time *Reinaert I* was written, part of the culture of the early Franks.

110. *Hulsterloo.* A wood below Hulst and Kieldrecht in Dutch Flanders.

111. *Krekenpit.* A spring or well from which flows a *kreek* (creek) near Hulst.

112. *May.* Mixtures of topographic and calendar designations emphasizing propinquity or remoteness were frequent, usually comic, and employed, for example, in medieval Latin, as in *inter Cluniacum et sancti festa Iohannis* and *inter Pascha Remisque.*

113. *Pater Simonet, the Friesian.* The reference in "Pater Simonet" is to simony; "the Friesian" has perhaps no significance since it may be the result of an error in transcribing *sies* (a type of hunting dog) present in this spot in one of the *Reinaert I* manuscripts.

114. *Rine.* J. W. Muller assumes the name to be the same as that of the Rhine River and adduces several hound names to support his assumption.

115. *Tiselin.* A name extending back to the *Roman*, where its form is *Tiesselin*, and ultimately of Germanic origin, its root being in old German * *Theod-.*

116. *Master Gelys.* In *Reinaert I* the name is *Jufroet*, from a form of old German * *Goda-frid*, and, according to J. W. Muller, here referring to Goeffroy d'Angers of the 12th century, a Benedictine and later a cardinal, or, according to D. C. Tinbergen, to Goeffroy's teacher Guillelmus.

117. *Prendelor.* A name made up from an Old French imperative phrase meaning "take the gold" and used first by the *Reinaert II* poet.

118. *Loosefind.* A name corresponding to *Loesvant* (sly trick) of the Gouda edition.

119. *Rapiamus.* A name consisting of an inflected Latin verb meaning "let us pillage" and used first by the *Reinaert II* poet.

120. *A pilgrim of deux as.* A pilgrim of little worth. The allusion is to a dice game where *deux* (two) and *as* (one) indicate a low score.

121. *He will pay for it if we fetch it.* A remark, where *he* refers to the king, implying "we can have anything at court — all we have to do is go there and pick it up."

122. *Wododekkis.* Stallybrass reads "woodcocks," Thoms and Arber as above. The microfilm of the printed text shows the above spelling clearly. The Gouda edition mentions "partridges" and "snipe." No reference work seems to have noticed this word, which, to be sure, could be a misprint.

123. *Elenge.* With this word Caxton translated the Middle Dutch adjective *elendich*, which can mean "foreign" or "exiled" or "miserable," the last sense being the proper one in English in 1481.

124. *Bokart.* The name of an animal, unspecified as to species, derived from an old German form of *Burkhard* via the Picard form *Bocart*, and in *Reynard* probably the byname of an ape, since in *Reynardus Vulpes* there is an ape *Boccardus*.

125. *Firapeel.* A name of Romance origin, probably derived from Old French *fier a pel* (proud of pelt).

126. *That I.* Not in the Gouda edition and probably a misprint.

127. *Tabard.* Here, as in the Gouda edition, a word meaning both a garment and a heraldic symbol of office.

128. *Lampreel.* A name, still present in Dutch as *lamprei* (young rabbit), derived from Old French *laperel* (young rabbit), which is cognate to modern French *lapin* (rabbit), itself of Germanic origin and cognate to modern German *Lappen* (lobe [of the ear]).

129. *Corbant.* A name of Romance origin related to modern French *corbeau* (crow) and appearing as *corbant* in the Gouda edition and *corbout* in *Reinaert II.*

130. *Sharpbeak.* A translation of the name *scerpenebbe* in the Gouda edition.

131. *Slonked.* Context indicates a signification "devoured," but just how Caxton arrived at *slonked* is not clear. The Gouda edition reads *stont ende at* (stood and ate) at this point. Middle Dutch *slinken / slank*, which could give *slonk* in Caxton's English, means "fall in," "sink down," and "grow lean" and would not fit the context here. *Slonked* seems to be adapted from Middle Dutch *(ver-)slingen / (ver-)slang* (devour/ devoured), not listed in Verdam's *Middelnederlandsch Handwoordenboek*, but present in the Gouda edition. A change from *slang* to *slonk* is conceivable, but Caxton's verb shows a weak preterite suffix, perhaps part of an attempt to anglicize the word. Finally, there may be in Caxton's *slonked* a fusion of two Middle Dutch verbs, the strong *(ver-)slingen* and the weak *slocken*, the latter

ANNOTATIONS

also meaning "to devour." *Slang* in the next sentence probably is the preterite of English *sling*.

132. *How he can stuff the sleeve with flocks.* The translation of the Gouda edition's *hoe maecte hi die mouwe . . . vol mit vlocken* (how he did make our sleeve full of flocks), which implies "how high-handedly he deceived us."

133. *Flee.* In the Gouda edition *ontvlyen* (fly away from), a reading which Muller and Logeman feel is an error for *ontlyven* (kill).

134. *Against him.* That is, "evidence enough against him to show."

135. *Brotherson.* An inconsistency and an addition to the Gouda edition by Caxton; elsewhere Grimbert is Reynard's sisterson.

136. *He spared neither bush nor haw.* The implication is that Grimbert jumped or plowed through bushes and hedges in his haste. *Highway* on the line above Caxton used to translate the Gouda edition's *den rechten wech* (the direct way).

137. *Loaded torches.* An attempt to translate *"toertsen . . . laden"* of the Gouda edition, which itself is a poor rendering of *laden ende trossen* (load and pack) of *Reinaert II*.

138. *Be in your word.* As much as, "have the floor."

139. *Reynardin.* A name, a diminutive form of *Reynard*, that became the favorite for Reynard's son in the 17th and 18th century English sequels to *Reynard the Fox*.

140. *Think not long.* As much as, "Do not yearn after me."

141. *It goes otherwhile by weening.* Things sometimes go unpredictably. *Goes by* may have meant to Caxton "goes counter to" and *weening* "expectation" and such at least is supported by the Gouda edition's *si gaet by wylen wtghissen*.

142. *Dowed.* From the *duwede* of the Gouda edition.

143. *Houthulst and Elverding.* The first is a wood, the second a town between Ypres and Diksmuide in West Flanders.

144. *Both laws.* That is, of the spiritual and temporal courts.

145. *Slept your dinner.* Slept off your dinner; corresponding to *verslapen* of the Gouda edition.

146. *Cantum.* Muller and Logeman suggest the high or melody-carrying part in church vocal music is here intended.

147. *Dool.* From the Gouda edition's *verdwalen* (go astray) and probably covered by the OED's *dull v.* II Intr. 6. "to become stupid."

148. *Hinder.* Reduced from a complete clause in the Gouda edition *mer dat v alre meest hinderen sal* (but that which shall hinder you most of all).

149. *He is not run away from his master.* The implication, accord-

ing to Muller and Logeman, is that he has not so early left his teacher that he lacks complete training.

150. *They.* That is, "people enjoying preferment."

151. *See through their fingers.* A translation from the Gouda edition of a phrase meaning "to close one's eyes when something unlawful is being done."

152. *Placebo.* A word meaning "something ingratiating (as a remark or act)," proverbial in English as "to sing placebo" meaning "to give lip service to."

153. *After amend it by counsel.* As much as, "Afterwards rectify it through shrewdness."

154. *Halt tofore you.* In the Gouda edition *soe dat nyemant voer v manck en mach gaen* (so that no one may precede you lamely). The sense is that "you take second place to no one."

155. *Would charge me.* "Evil shrews" is meant to be the subject.

156. *I cry out harrow.* Here the sense is very close to "I denounce."

157. *I must here through how that I do.* Caxton's words translate *Ic moet hier doch doer so hoe dat icket make* (I must nevertheless [go] through [with it] here, howsoever I manage it) of the Gouda edition.

158. *From myself.* Beside myself.

159. *Doling.* Caxton's word reflects the Middle Dutch *dolen* (wander) rather than the Middle English *dolen* (grieve).

160. *Martin.* In Flanders an old name for a monkey, attested as early as the fourteenth century in English in the form *martyn apen*, and derived from the Latin *Martininus.*

161. *Camerick.* Cambray. Various Reynard annotators point to a thirteenth century religious house that attained some notoriety as the reason for Cambray's being used here.

162. *Touch charge.* Pertain to weighty matters, the sense suggested by the Gouda edition's *saken die last dragen.*

163. *Et vos estote parati.* As in Matthew 24:44 and Luke 12:40.

164. *I helped him that he went from him.* Here the first *him* refers to Lampreel and the second to Reynardin. *Went* is Caxton's translation of the Gouda edition's *ontquam* (escaped).

165. *Thus came I in the word and am not laid in the blame.* The sense seems to be "thus I got into trouble and am no part of the injustice."

166. *Borne on hand.* An idiom, usually entered in glosses as *bear in hand*, meaning "delude (as by pretenses)."

167. *Simon, my eme.* An allusion to simony. Compare annotation 113.

ANNOTATIONS

168. *Prentout.* A name made up of an Old French phrase meaning "take all."

169. *Waitscathe.* Printed *wayte scathe* by Caxton, *Wayte, Scathe* by Morley and Stallybrass, and *Waytescathe* by Thoms. It translates *luuster vele* (Listen-Much), *scalck vont* (Cunning-Trick), or *Ghif mi een greep* (Give-Me-a-Handful) of the Gouda edition. Henryson uses it as a wolf's name in his *Morall Fabillis.* It means "one who waits to do injury."

170. *The prayer is with gifts hardy.* The implication is that an appeal accompanied by a gift can be bolder than one made without a gift.

171. *Rukenaw.* A name derived from Middle Dutch meaning "smell enough."

172. *For blood must creep where it cannot go.* The expression means here that blood ties continue to exist even if strained.

173. *It skills not.* It makes no difference.

174. *Pope's palace of Woerden.* In the Gouda edition *des paeus hof van weerden*, probably "the Pope's splendid court," which Caxton mistranslated, assuming *van weerden* (of splendor) to be the name of a town — *Werden* or *Woerden.*

175. *Hold.* Probably Caxton means "withhold itself," but the Gouda edition reads *Man en sal dat recht doer nyement mencken* (One shall not distort the law for any man).

176. *Estote misericordes.* As in Luke 6:36.

177. *Nolite iudicare et non iudicabimini.* As in Matthew 7:1.

178. The phraseology is from the Bible (Matthew 7:3 and Luke 6:41), but the now common vernacular words are *mote* (for Caxton's *straw*) and *beam* (for Caxton's *balk*).

179. *The honor and worship of him that he has done.* Put more simply, "the honor and credit he has gained."

180. *Me.* The impersonal pronoun meaning "one" that translates the *men* of the Gouda edition and that in Caxton's day was somewhat rare in both its *me* and *men* forms.

181. *Parable.* Rukenaw's tale is relevant because it recalls Reynard's past deserts, puts Isegrim and Bruin in a bad light, and warns the king that due process of law should be observed, but the tale falls out of the character of the early Flemish Reynard epic by treating man and animal on the same level, as does also the tale, related somewhat later, of the horse and stag graven on the miraculous looking glass.

182. *I may do it good tofore all the world that I do.* More simply, "I may well before the whole world do what I do."

212

183. *Slindpere*. A name adapted from the Gouda edition's *slijnde-pier* (devour the worm).

184. *That do, let the sentence go*. The sense is "if that is done, then let the sentence fall."

185. *Ill on enough*. Badly enough off.

186. *Emptybelly and Neverfull*. Caxton's translation of *ydelbalch ende nymmersat* of the Gouda edition.

187. *Blasen*. A word meaning "blow" that was archaic in Caxton's day in the native form deriving from Old Norse *blása*.

188. *Avincenna*. The Persian physician, philosopher, and commentator on Aristotle, Abu Ibn Sin Avicenna (980–1036).

189. *At the long*. In the end.

190. *Growl*. Groan; here used with an accusative impersonal pronoun (*him*), the second *him* referring to Reynard.

191. *We will forbear you*. This and the two following clauses appear, perhaps with greater clarity, in the Gouda edition as: *wi willen v verdraghen ghi en moget ons niet missegghen noch om v en seg ics oeck niet* (We desire to bear with you. You can neither say anything harmful to us nor do I say this on your account), but neither version is particularly smooth.

192. *Him*. Here referring somewhat awkwardly to Reynard, although in the Gouda edition referring to the "three full-waxen children."

193. *Bitelouse*. Caxton's version of the Gouda edition's *biteluys*.

194. *Fullrump*. The Gouda edition reads *vulromp* (foul body).

195. *Hatenette*. The Gouda edition reads *hatenete* (hate the nit).

196. *Nephew*. Here simply "young relative," for Reynard would be the cousin of Rukenaw's children.

197. *Mousehound*. In Caxton spelled *musehont*, entered in the OED as *mousehunt*, appearing in the Gouda edition as *muushont*, and meaning in Middle Dutch either cat or weasel, but in *Reynard the Fox* probably the latter since Tibert has already appeared. Caxton's spelling of *mouse* is elsewhere *mows*, but he may have thought the Middle Dutch form he printed in 1481 would be transparent enough to his countrymen so that he could let it stand in its original — or nearly original — form.

198. *Ordegele*. A name in its Old French form meaning "dirty scab."

199. *Ostrole*. In *Reinaert II* the byname of the martin, but assumed to be a species name by the Gouda editor and hence separated from "the martin" in context. The origin of the name is not clear.

200. *Pantecroet*. A name of unknown etymology.

201. *Atrote.* A name of unknown etymology.
202. *She has the rise do blossom again.* She has made the twig blossom again.
203. *Look out of my eyes.* Keep my eyes open.
204. *Master Akerin.* A name for which commentators have found no convincing etymology.
205. *Curse for them in all churches.* The Gouda edition is clear: *in alle kerken to banne doen die daer of weten* (excommunicate in all churches those who know thereof).
206. *Abrion of Trier.* Perhaps a name that evolved from Aaron or Abraham.
207. *Strangullion.* A disease of horses causing the throat glands to swell and become inflamed.
208. *Panthera.* The sweet-smelling panther of Physiologus.
209. *Cybore.* In the Gouda edition *cybor.* A word for which a satisfactory gloss has yet to be given; it is probably a color, since in *Reinaert II* the word here is *sinoper* (green [in heraldry]).
210. *Everything by himself.* Everything by itself, that is "separately."
211. *King Crompart.* The allusion here and in what follows is to the *Roman de Cleomades ou le cheval de fust*, which Adenes li Rois versified c. 1280.
212. *But the most . . . of the wood.* But almost everything occurred through the power of the wood.
213. *Mysteries.* The Gouda edition here reads *hystorien* (histories or romances).
214. *Have thank hereof.* Have recompense for this.
215. *With his fifteen.* That is, "with fifteen others like him."
216. *Sikerness.* Here the sense is close to "fidelity," one of the basic senses of the Middle Dutch word *zekerheit*, which stands in this spot in the Gouda edition.
217. *So that another did it.* Implying "so long as another individual caused the harm."
218. *Though so were.* Although it was.
219. *But it was a rasing against his death.* A bad translation in the Gouda edition of the portion in *Reinaert II*:

> Met het was seker tegens synen doot
> Hy wart von synnen zeer wonderlic
> groot
> Dat hi so raesde ende dutte

But it was certain about his [Noble's father's] approaching death: he was very strangely out of his head so that he raged and raved.

220. *And the wise . . . lords oft lack.* Caxton's rendering of the Gouda edition's *die wijsheit die wort verdruct des hebben die heren groet afterdeel* (wisdom is crushed; therefore the lords suffer great disadvantage).

221. *Unroused be it.* An expression of doubtful meaning, perhaps equivalent to "unnoticed as it was," since in the Gouda edition the word it corresponds to is *onuerweten* (unrecognized). Punctuation and sentence division in this section of Caxton's text is problematic; several possibilities seem open. The OED apparently does not cover the word *unroused*, at least in this sense.

222. *Reynard.* Omitted in the printed text of 1481.

223. *Stretched him.* A phrase implying "exaggerated his importance."

224. *I should deserve against you.* A sentence that translates *ic souts v lonen* (I should reward you for it) of the Gouda edition.

225. *Bore my wife on hand.* Deluded my wife.

226. *Blow with all winds.* A proverbial expression here equivalent in meaning to "how craftily he can shift his ground."

227. *Await if I did not for him there.* Just wait to hear how I took care of him there.

228. *Laid down.* From the Gouda edition's *gelegen* (confined in childbed).

229. *Shall think long after me.* Must wonder where I am, translating *sal nae mij verlanghen* (probably are longing for me) of the Gouda edition.

230. *Me growls of.* I am revolted by.

231. *What may I do thereto?* What can I do about it?

232. *What lies that in your way?* How does that concern you?

233. *Proof.* Probably meaning here "show," a sense corresponding to the Gouda edition's *proels* (bombast).

234. *Proof.* Probably meaning here "high-sounding words," a sense corresponding to the Gouda edition's *proelen.*

235. *Boudelo.* An abbey in Waesland, founded in 1105.

236. *Glat.* Smooth. Caxton's word here is the one in the Gouda edition and apparently never became part of the English vocabulary.

237. *Handsel.* Here to be interpreted as "an unrequested gift which may bring good luck with it."

238. *Were. Was* is in the printed text of 1481.

239. *Dared.* Probably in the sense "hurt," which is the sense of the Gouda edition's *deerde.*

240. *Buff nor haff.* Essentially an interjection, but here, if possessed

of any meaning at all, to be taken as "anything" and corresponding to *boe noch bau* of the Gouda edition.

241. *Stuffs.* Probably "matter," but with suggestions of the meaning "dust," since the word here in the Gouda edition is *stoff* (dust).

242. *Rowm.* Far; not from OE *rúm*, but from Middle Dutch *rume* of the Gouda edition. (The OED listing of this passage under *room* 1c is questionable.)

243. *Prize.* A word corresponding to *eeren* (honor) of the Gouda edition.

244. *Overthrow.* Caxton here undoubtedly intended "fall down," since the Gouda edition here reads *stortede neder.*

245. *Might best over me.* Perhaps the sense is closely followed in the words "might be in an advantageous position if opposing me."

246. *Withholden.* Esteemed, a sense indicated by *ghesien* of the Gouda edition.

247. *Happen.* In modern idiom, "turn out to be."

248. *Growled them.* They were horrified.

249. *This right.* A phrase incorrectly derived by Caxton from the Gouda edition's *dit ghereht* (this meal), referring to the stolen bone of the parable. Caxton's translation of the parable that follows is occasionally shaky and inaccurate.

250. *Shorn.* Molested, a word that is equivalent to the *-bescoren* of the Gouda edition.

251. *After behind.* An awkward translation of *achter ten sterte wert* (back toward the tail), referring to the scalded dog of the preceding parable, at least in the Gouda edition.

252. *Let him these extortions in their sorrow and need.* The whole preceding paragraph is somewhat disturbing in that it is not always easy to determine whom the pronouns refer to. The fault, however, is not wholly Caxton's, since the Gouda edition is itself not altogether clear in its references.

253. *Bear them on hand of.* Delude them with.

254. *To my power.* Implying "as much as I could."

255. *The best that I can, do.* Clearly, "do the best that I can"; the punctuation, which makes an otherwise mystifying sentence clear, is probably the work of Morley.

256. *For they be his words and not mine.* Caxton's addition, which recalls Chaucer's words in the "Nun's Priest's Tale" (line 3265): "These been the cokkes words, and not myne."

GLOSSARY

aby: atone for
adventure: (1) risk (2) fortune
afterdeal: disadvantage
aggravate: excommunicated
algates: notwithstanding
also: so
apaid: pleased
appeached: accused
appealed: (1) accused (2) invited
arette: ascribe
assoil: absolve
avaunting: praising
avowtry: adultery
awreak: requite
back: bat
bail: bailiff
ballock stone: testicle
ban: curse
bebled: bloody
bedrive: (1) carry on (2) plot
bedwing: subdue
bedwongen: (1) governed (2) compelled
behoveful: useful
belikes: resembles
benam: took
beneme: take from
berisp: censure
betel: wedge
betimes: early
bewimple: envelop
bewray: expose
bills: pickaxes
bleef: tarried
bombards: stone-throwing cannons
boots: cures

borrows: pledges
bourd: joke
boussing: polecat
bracing: swaggering
broke: (1) transgression (2) offense
brook: use
bules: swellings
burg: fortress
camping: fighting
can: knows
car: cart
casus: ABC's
cetyne: shittim wood
charge: (1) straits (2) burden
cheer: mien
cite: summon to court
clergy: learning
clope: blow
close: hermitage
coif: skullcap
come off: hurry
comprise: comprehend
con: be able to
conceit: esteem
conceive: apprehend
conditions: personal qualities
coney: rabbit
conjure: implore
cost: food
cratched: scratched
cullion: testicle
Dan: Sir
dasse: badger
day: summon
dazzled: clouded over
delved: buried

217

depart: divide
dere: grieve
despite: contempt
devoir: duty
dier: animal
dispiteously: mercilessly
disposed: conducted
disworshipped: disgraced
dompt: tame
dool: become dull
dools: errs
doubt: fear
dowed: (1) nipped (2) squeezed
dread: peril
drove: drifted
dubbed: struck
elenge: miserable
eme: uncle
enterprise: attempt
ermed: grieved
erst: sooner
esbatements: amusements
eschew: avoid
even: fellow
everydeal: everything
facing: boasting
falldoor: trap door
famed: imaginary
fell: cruel
felly: cruelly
ferners: times
flawnes: flat cakes
flindermouse: bat
flitch: side
flume: river
forborne: tolerated
fordeal: (1) advantage (2) opportunity
fordo: thwart
fordrive: (1) drive away (2) persecute
forfrozen: frozen fast

forhungered: starved
formably: elegantly
forslingered: beat
forslongen: devoured
forth: further
forthon: henceforth
forwitting: reproach
forwrought: ruined
frank: clear
galped: yelped
genet: civet cat
genitors: genitals
ghostly: spiritual
ghostly: holily
glimmed: glimmered
glozed: flattered
gobbet: chunk
grate: fishbone
grim: grow angry
grin: snare
grise: costly grey fur
harness: genital
haunt: practice
haw: hedge
hebenus: ebony
herefore: therefore
hermel: ermine
him: himself
hovedance: court dance
inwit: understanding
irous: angry
jape: joke
knowledge: acknowledge
lapwinches: lapwings
leave: neglect
lene: bestow something on
lering: doctrine
lesings: deceits
let: (1) stop (2) hinder
lettings: hindrances
lickerous: greedy
lief: dear

likeness: parable
list: desired
lists: barriers
locked: enticed
longen: belong
lose: renown
loss: lynx
lust: delight
lusty: merry
mail: bag
mainour: plunder
manchets: loaves of fine white bread
mandment: commandment
mathes: maggots
meat: food
meercat: monkey
meinie: household
member: limb
minished: deleted
misdid: harmed
misfall: misfortune
misfell: mischanced
misprized: scorned
missake: renounce
morrowtide: morningtide
mote: (1) must (2) may
muggets: intestines
nickers: water monsters
noble: coin
or: before
ordained: contrived
orgulous: haughty
otherwhile: sometimes
overcharged: accused excessively
overest: supreme
overnice: very foolish
paid: pleased
palster: pilgrim's staff
peased: appeased
piked: made off
pilch: cloak

pill: pillage
plain: complain
plat: flat
plat: quite
pudding: sausage
queans: sluts
quit: (1) free (2) repay
rat: wheel
raught: reached
ravener: plunderer
ravin: gluttony
recipes: prescriptions
reprised: reproached
retch: care
ribald: knave
ridge: back
rised: traveled
room: area
roomed: left
rore: stir
rover: robber
roving: plundering
row: rough
rumor: uproar
rutsel: slide
scat: treasure
scat: tax
scathed: hurt
scrabbing: clawing
scrip: wallet
seethe: boil
seld: seldom
shamefast: modest
shawm: an oboe-like instrument
shrew: rogue
shrewd: evil
sib: kin
sikerly: surely
sith: hand
sith: (1) since (2) afterwards
skill: (1) judge (2) mean
slavin: mantle

219

slepped: dragged
slipper: slippery
slonked: devoured
smeke: flatter
smoldered: smothered
snell: quick
sodden: boiled
sold: hire
sonderly: especially
sorrowed: provided
sped: handled
spind: pantry
spitey: spiteful
spitous: spiteful
stool: throne
stoundmeal: at intervals
strait: strict
strike: snare
striked: hastened
strong: flagrant
strop: loop
tabard: mantle
tasted: (1) felt (2) reached
tattling: faltering
tho: then
thorpe: town
to: thereto
tobeaten: beaten to pieces
tobroken: broken
tofore: before
tokens: details
totorn: shredded
tree: wood
turns: wrongs
unberisped: undisturbed
under: between
underdelved: buried thereunder

uneath: hardly
ungeluck: misfortune
unhap: misfortune
unshamefast: shameless
unthrifts: no goods
vane: banner
vysevase: folly
wain: wagon
wapper: truncheon
wappered: slugged
warned: denied
waxen: grown
ween: think
wentle: twist
whereas: where
wight: fellow
wike: withdraw
wine: friend
winning: gain
wist: knew
wit: know
wite: blame
withoutforth: on the outside
wonderly: surprising
woned: accustomed
wood: mad
worden: became
worship: (1) credit (2) honor
wot: know
wrake: revenge
wrawen: meow
wreak: avenge
wrived: rubbed
yammered: grieved
yonned: wished
yonst: favor

INDEX

Aachen, 86
Abrion of Trier, 141
Aesopic fable, 34
Akerin, 140
Antwerp *Reynard de Vos*, see Antwerp *volksboek* of 1564
Antwerp *volksboek* of 1564, 8, 11
Araby, 109
Ardennes, 85
Aristotle, 137
Arnout, 24
Arnout-Perrot controversy, 19
Asia, 144
Atrote, 139
Ave Abelquak, 60
Avicenna, 137

Baetkin, 60
Baldwin the Young, 26
Bave, 60
Bellin the ram, 78; does mass, 97 f; delivers Cuwart's head to Noble, 102 ff; given as peace offering to Bruin, Isegrim, and Erswind, 106 ff
Bertolt, 60
Bishop of Camerik, 124
Bitelouse, 167
Blades, William: error in comment on Caxton's *Reynard*, 10–11
Bokart, the king's secretary, 105
Borre the bull, 79
Boudelo, 167
Boudewin the ass, 79, 147
Brink, Bernard ten, 39
Browning, 55
Bruges, 32; French cultural predominence in, 33
Bruin the bear, 54; sent to summon Reynard, 54 ff; enticed into Lantfert's yard, 57 ff; beaten by Lantfert and the villagers, 59 ff

Brunel the goose, 79
Byles, A. T. P., 38

Cambridge Fragments, 10–11
Cantart, 51
Caxton, William, 3; relative number of surviving first editions, 4; paradoxical life, 31; Low German stay, 31–32; business success, 32–33; introduction of the comic beast epic, 34; *Esope*, 35; lexicographic significance, 36; syntax, 36; prose style, 36–37; treatment by modern critics, 37–39
Caxton's *Reynard the Fox, see History of Reynard the Fox, The*
Chanticleer the cock, 51; leads funeral entourage of his daughter Coppen, 51 ff
Charles, Duke of Burgundy, 33
Charles the Great, 39
Cleomedes, 145
Cologne, 123
Colvile, K. N., 37
Coppen, 51; her burial, 54
Corbant the rook, 108; complains to Noble over death of his wife, 108 ff
Crayant, 51
Crompart, 145
Culemann, Senator F. G. H., 11
Culemann Fragments, *see* Cambridge Fragments
Curtois the hound, 48; lodges complaint against Reynard, 48
Cuwart the hare, 48; abused by Reynard, 48 ff; stands as proof of King Ermerik's treasure, 92 f; slain by Reynard, 100

Delft edition of *Reynaert*, 8

Loosefind, 98
Louis de Bruges, 33
Lübeck edition of 1498, *see Keinke de Vos*
Ludolf, 60
Lydgate, John, 35

Macob, 60
Maleperduys, 51; description, 55
Malory, Thomas, 31
Mansion, Colard, 33
Margaret, Duchess of Burgundy, 33
Marie de France, 35
Martin the ape, 124; offers to help in defending Reynard, 124 ff; tells Reynard he can put the whole court under the Pope's curse, 126 ff
Martinet, 67
Meer, Jacob Jacobzoon van der, 8
Menelaus, 144
Merchant Adventurers, 32
Mierlo, Jan van: as a voice against the multiple authorship of *Reinaert I*, 24–25
Montpelier, 66, 151
Morcadiga, 145
Muller, Jacob W., his criticism of *Reinaert II*, 16–18
Muller, J. W., and Henri Logeman: comment on *Die hystorie van Reinaert die Vos*, 11–13

Neverfull, 135
Nivardus of Ghent, 28
Noble the lion, 77; calls together his court, 45 ff; allows Reynard to go free as a pilgrim, 90 ff; calls a second feast to placate Bruin and Isegrim, 107
"Nonnes Prestes Tale," 35

Odo of Cheriton, 35
Olewey the ewe, 78
Ordegale, 178
Ottram, 60

Pallas, 143
Pantecroet, wife of the otter, 138, 178
Panthera, 143
Paris, 143
Pentecost, 45
Pertilot, 79
Pierre de St. Cloud, 23–24
Plomer, Henry R., 38
Pogge of Chafport, 60
Prendelor, 98
Prentout, 126
Priamus, 144

Rapiamus, 98
Recuyell of the Historyes of Troye, 31–32, 36
Reinaert I, 14; manuscripts, 19–20; prologue, 20–21; the problem of French and Flemish sources, 21–25
Reinaert II: as source of *Die hystorie van Reynaert die Vos*, 11; manuscripts, 14–15; its poet, 15; adverse criticism, 15–18; prologue, 18
Reinaerts Historie, see Reinaert II
Reinardus Vulpes, 5, 26–27
Reineke Fuchs, 15
Reinhart Fuchs, 28
Reinke de Vos, 11, 15
Reynard the fox: character, 3; tradition, 5; popularity 1475–1500, 12; absent from court, 46; approaches Chanticleer as a pilgrim, 52 f; confesses his sins to Grimbert, 71 ff; tells of taking a capon off the priest's table, 73 f; sentenced to be hanged, 80 ff; confesses his sins by the gallows, 82 ff; relates conspiracy against Noble, 85 ff; tells lie about King Ermerik's treasure, 91 ff; describes his offspring, 114 f; bids adieu to his household, 115 f; confesses his sins to Grimbert a second time, 116 ff; confesses the reason for his corruption, 119

DATE DUE

Demco, Inc. 38-293